Songs for Sixpence

Songs for Sixpence

A Story About John Newbery

BY JOSEPHINE BLACKSTOCK

Illustrated by Maurice Bower

Follett Publishing Company

NEW YORK   CHICAGO   TORONTO

Author's Foreword

I have asked several hundred people—they were all ages, children, mothers, and grandmothers—what tales they remember best; and most of them said Mother Goose. We owe this name for our nursery rhymes to an eighteenth-century English bookseller—John Newbery, the first publisher to make something of a specialty of children's books. He lived back before the American Revolution, and one of his many books was among the earliest collections of nursery rhymes, and among the best. It was called *Mother Goose's Melody*, and it was reprinted again and again for American children, with more and more additions, long after John Newbery was dead and the American Colonies had become the United States of America.

Though the Newbery Award for the most distinguished American children's book of the year is named in honor of John Newbery, not many people know much about him. I enjoyed reading about him and about his author friends and about English life in the seventeen hundreds and the first children's books. There is only one biography of John Newbery, but fortunately he was a good friend of such famous authors as Oliver Goldsmith and Samuel Johnson, and London literary society in the eighteenth century is very well reported. Much of Dr. Johnson's conversation in this book, for instance, is made up of things he is actually known to have said.

John Newbery's contribution to children's books was important, and there is much information to be found on that. One of the most interesting pieces of literary detective work I have come across is the discussion of *Mother Goose's Melody* and its probable date and the reasons for thinking that Goldsmith wrote the preface, in the introduction to the *Oxford Dictionary of Nursery Rhymes*. Some of Newbery's little books are still in existence. They would seem very quaint to modern children, and yet the best of them— *Mother Goose's Melody*, for example, which was so well-loved that it survives only in later reprints—are delightful. John Newbery himself was a delightful man, and I hope that this story presents him as I came to know him from his life and works and from the way his friends described him. He was not a genius or a hero, but he must have been one of the nicest ordinary men in a very interesting period of history. And all children who read books owe a great deal to the little London bookseller, John Newbery.

JOSEPHINE BLACKSTOCK

For Ruth Whitfield,
Good teacher, good friend

Songs for Sixpence

*W*IFE, wherever *is* that lad?"

Farmer Newbery scowled as he came tramping into the kitchen. He held a stable lantern in one hand, a brimming pail of milk in the other. Setting down the pail, he blew out the light and threw himself down on the settle.

CHAPTER *One*

"You be upsetting yourself over naught, Robert," his wife said, pulling her shawl tighter about her shoulders. September mornings in Berkshire could be chilly at times.

"So it is naught that the horse is unfed, there is no wood for the fire, and the hogwash is still in the kitchen?" Farmer Newbery's voice was sharp. "And to top it all, I found rats in the corn this morning!"

"Get you out to the wash-up, Robert, and take the muck off your hands. The porridge is ready."

Mrs. Newbery was stooping over an iron pot that hung from a crane on the hearth. She gave it one last stir and pulled the crane away from the fire.

Farmer Newbery was too put out to bother about any dirty hands. He stayed hunched on the settle, frowning.

"Here's Bob away helping his grandfather," he said, "and nary a sign of John since cockcrow. He's all of eleven years old; why can't he set his shoulder to the wheel same as you and me and his brother?"

Mrs. Newbery sighed softly. "Save when his nose is in a book, John is the best son a body could want. 'Tis the printed word that makes him forget to eat or sleep."

"That's it!" Farmer Newbery's fist thumped down on the settle. "He's fair moon-struck over reading. How did you and me ever have a son like him?"

12

"Stop your complaining, Robert, and set you down and eat. *I* have no time to waste over words, even if you have. I must take pail and brush on these kitchen bricks and sand the floor anew."

But Farmer Newbery was still muttering to himself as he pulled up a bench to the table. He loved his son John, but of late the lad was forever making him lose his temper. A country boy hankering to read, when by rights he ought to be doing his chores! A body was poor; even with the good crops of the last few years—it was 1724—he must toil from sunup to dark to make ends meet. Sowing, harrowing, reaping, carrying the crops to market; year round, just one thing after another! Robert Newbery frowned as he dipped his horn spoon into the hot gruel. Lackaday! And now even the neighbors were beginning to look at John like he was a colt with three legs.

He finished his breakfast and put down his spoon. "Wife," he said, "my mind is made up. I'll have a plain talk with the lad, and if he don't give me his word he'll settle down to business, I'll let him have a taste of the birch that he'll not soon forget."

Mrs. Newbery said not a word as she gathered up the wooden bowls and set them in the washing pot. Could John have got this queer reading craze from that ancestor of his father's, Ralph Newbery? Him that published books way

13

back in Good Queen Bess's time? Might a lad—she shook her head perplexedly—might a lad inherit a liking for books the same as he could inherit the shape of his nose? In other ways, John was a good and proper boy, kindhearted and industrious. A lively playing lad, as well.

If only Dame Dorcas would speak to him! Suddenly Mrs. Newbery stood quite still, letting the dishclout drip on her apron. Yes, she would ask Dame Dorcas; it was the only thing left to do. Dame Dorcas was the mistress of the village school, and John set great stock by her. *She* must persuade the lad where his duty lay; wasn't that what a teacher was for?

"Robert," Mrs. Newbery started to say, but then she stopped.

John himself was standing there in the door, his eyes shining, his cheeks all red, and, sure enough, a book in his hand.

"Mother, just look!" His voice was ringing. "Master Monk, he lent me this book of *Robinson Crusoe*. It makes a body's heart fair skip. The ship is wrecked close by an island, and—"

"Afore George, your back is going to be wrecked, too, when I'm done with 'ee!" Mr. Newbery had jumped to his feet, both his hands clenched. "No son of mine is going to turn out a lazy good-for-naught, not if *I* knows it. Sneaking off afore your chores is even started!"

"I—I'm sorry, Father. I forgot." John's voice was ashamed and scared. "Don't trounce me this time, please. I'll make it up to you, I promise I will."

"Come here," said Mr. Newbery grimly.

"Father, I—I'll work like a horse. The wood will be brought and the carrots weeded before you can say Jack Robinson—two times."

The rod in his hand, Mr. Newbery hesitated. John was a lad to be proud of in looks. He was short, but he had a straight way of holding himself, and there was good color in his cheeks. His eyes were clear and honest, and his threadbare smock and breeches couldn't hide his healthy body. Why in the name of goodness did he have this queer streak in him?

Mr. Newbery sighed. Well, what was there left to do but break the lad's will with a taste of the rod? 'Twas what a father was for. Most every Sunday, Parson said as much. A man spared the birch, and he spoiled the child.

He lifted his head slowly; he lifted it just in time to see John whisking out through the door. Mr. Newbery turned to his wife and shook his head. It was she must have given the boy the nod to duck off. What could you do with a soft-hearted woman like her?

A LARK was climbing up the sky; you could see the flash of its wings out the window. Robins were whistling, and a dog barked. Inside the little schoolroom, though, there was no sound except for Dame Dorcas's voice, going on and on. The boys were sitting on benches on one side of the room, the

CHAPTER *Two*

girls on the other. A picture of King George hung on one whitewashed wall, and a small pile of shabby books lay on the desk.

"That is all for the counting lesson, children. Fold your hands on your laps."

Dame Dorcas was straightening her tiny body as she spoke. She was not much taller than a twelve-year-old herself. Her graying hair was neatly tucked inside her clean mobcap; the kerchief crossed on her linsey-woolsey bodice was spotless. Her face was as brown as a walnut, but her eyes were bright and alert.

"Yes, Dame," chorused the children.

"Hannah, you are to wear the marker this morning; *both* your sums were wrong. You said that two plus three was six and one taken away from seven was five." Dame Dorcas was hanging the paper marker on a string around the little girl's neck. "Do not forget, child," she said, "that diligence is the mother of success."

"No, ma'am," Hannah said meekly.

"John Newbery, please to come here."

John gave a start and blushed. His thoughts had been a thousand miles away. He had been striding along a stretch of sand, meeting Man Friday, telling him about the shipwreck.

"Yes, Dame," he said, stumbling up the aisle.

"I propose to try an experiment, John." Dame Dorcas's voice was brisk and tart. "It happens that you are the best speller in school; so I am going to ask you to hear the younger children say their hornbook lesson whilst I instruct the older girls in knitting.

"But you older lads, don't imagine you are going to laze. Some will fetch in firewood, some fill the water bucket. Well, John, why aren't you getting to work?"

"I—I am going to, Dame."

John's mouth was gaping; his cheeks were as red as the holly berries outside the door. He chosen to be a teacher! It was like the end of the world had come. And the way everyone was staring at him! He could see Henry Monk fair goggle-eyed and the girls nudging one another and whispering.

"Don't think, John, that I shan't be keeping my eye on you, either." As she spoke, Dame Dorcas had begun to herd the girls to the back of the room.

John got a hornbook at the desk and sat down on a stool in front of the little children. The hornbook was made of wood, and it was shaped like a paddle. A sheet of paper was stretched over it, and over the paper was nailed a piece of yellowish horn. The alphabet was printed on the paper, in both large and small letters; there were syllables, too, like Ba, Be, Bo, and the Lord's Prayer. The two upper corners of the page

19

were covered with rows of crosses; this was the reason that a recitation from a hornbook was called "reading the crisscross rows."

"Rafe, please to read this." John was pointing with a quill at the Lord's Prayer as he spoke. Oh, if only the twelve faces wouldn't stare at him so hard! They could see how his hand was shaking and how his cheeks had gone red as a turkey cock.

Seven-year-old Rafe wriggled. He wiped his nose on his

sleeve. Rafe was a deal more interested in butterflies, earthworms, and snails than he was in reading. He stood up and rubbed one leg against the other.

"A, B, C, D," he blurted out.

"That child's stupidity fair tries one's patience," said Dame Dorcas sharply. (Goodness! She must have eyes in the back of her head, John thought.) "Paddle his hand, John, and make him feel it."

"Yes, ma'am," John said hoarsely.

Slowly he turned over the hornbook. Since it was made of wood, the hornbook made a good paddle for the hands of unlucky spellers and readers. John knew *that*; many were the times he'd felt its print on his palm when he was small. He winced now. Poor little Rafe! It was mortal hard for him to learn. If there were but a picture on the hornbook, now, something bright-colored and cheery-like, maybe he'd *want* to find out how to read.

"Did you hear me, John?" Dame Dorcas asked.

"Please, must I?" John's voice was begging. "Rafe is awful little, and besides he does know a deal about birds' nests and such."

"Hoity toity! Do as you are bid, John Newbery."

So, while Rafe sniffled and blubbered, John reluctantly did as he was bid.

21

"There, blow your nose, Rafe. Here's a kerchief."
Dame Dorcas handed the little boy a clean rag. "Susan," she
said, "you have dropped a stitch; I can see it from here. Now,
John, proceed with Molly."

"Please to spell out those three letters." John was pointing
again to the hornbook.

Molly Monk gulped and pulled at a curl; she didn't say
anything. John threw a glance at Dame Dorcas's back; surely
she couldn't see him now. John's lips silently spelt out, "X, Y,
Izzard."

"X, Y, Izzard," Molly chirruped happily.

"Now, Molly, will you—"

John got no further; there was a knock at the door, and
Dame Dorcas darted across the room to open the door. It was
John's mother. John gasped. This was a bit too much to happen to a body all on one day. First to be made teacher, and
then Mother coming here. She had never before done this;
something must be amiss. Swallowing hard, John stared at
her. She had on her Sunday-go-to-meeting shawl over her best
brown dress and her good bonnet, too, with the ribbons. She
didn't seem like herself; her face was white, and she looked
scared.

"Good morning to you, Mistress Newbery," Dame Dorcas said crisply.

"G-good morrow, D-dame." Mother was stammering.

"Is there something wrong? You look pale, Mistress New-bery."

"I'm mortal sorry to disturb you this way, Dame, but would you be so kind as to let me speak to you outside? With John there, too."

"And leave my pupils alone?" Dame stopped; she was looking very hard at Mother's worried face. Then her head gave a little jerk. "Very well, then. Children, mind your manners whilst I am gone."

The door closed. They were standing beneath the holly tree.

"I will thank you, Mistress Newbery, to be brief and to the point." Dame Dorcas was tapping her foot on the ground and frowning.

"Yes, Dame." John could see that his mother was trembling. "You *do* hold with the saying, Honor thy father and thy mother?"

"To be sure I do!"

"Alack! That is what ails my lad. He won't do the chores that are set him. Now his father is so angered that he wants to beat him and make his food dry crusts and water."

"Mother, please not to say any more," John pleaded.

She was not listening; she just went rushing on.

23

"It's all the fault of those pesky books, Dame. They are the lad's undoing. I don't know what he will come to—"

"Pesky books, you say!" Dame Dorcas broke in. "Pray, what do you mean by that?"

"John would sooner read than eat. Oh, don't think his father and I don't know what he is up to, wasting hour after hour lying on that straw pallet up in the attic! He is fair devouring some book or other."

"Am I the lad's father, Mistress Newbery?" Now Dame Dorcas's arms were folded across her chest.

"No, but you *are* his preceptress." Mother was wringing her hands. "If you could but see your way to tell the lad where his duty lies! 'Tis his father's fondest hope he be a farmer after him, but 'twas but yesterday John ran away for hours, just to lay his hand on some piddling book about one Robinson Crewe—"

"*Crusoe*, Mother, and 'tis a marvelous fine story, too." To his horror, John could feel tears prickling his eyelids. "Dame, please to listen. Crusoe is shipwrecked on a wondrous island and lives there all alone for years till he finds a kind black man who—"

"Tush, John, do you think I don't know that that tale is meat and drink to any lad?"

"But, Dame," Mother cried, "book learning is not for poor

24

country lads. It fills their heads with fine notions that can only come to naught. Oh, you must see that!"

"If I remember aright, it was a poor country lad, name of Dick Whittington, who became Lord Mayor of London!" Dame Dorcas's lips were quirking in a tiny smile. "Though John, here, has no cat to help him."

"Oh, yes, I have, ma'am. Her name is Tabitha."

"Then you may yet be a second Dick Whittington. But, Mistress Newbery, 'tis my considered opinion that you should encourage your son John in his book learning; we have dolts enough now in this countryside, and to spare. This lad already knows how to read three-syllable words, he can cast up any common sum, and he is the best speller in my school. Goodness, it would not surprise me if one of these days John Newbery wrote books himself!"

He, John, write books! His own ears had heard Dame Dorcas say so. John wet his lips, but no sound came.

"But, ma'am," his mother said faintly, "fair words, spoke or writ, butter no parsnips. 'Tis deeds that count."

"Fiddle-de-dee!" Dame had drawn erect every inch of her five feet. "This lad can recite the names of every king of England straight down to George the First, and he knows by heart the boundaries of England, France, and Spain. The love of books is a mark of sense, and you should thank God that He

25

has given you a son with brains, instead of worrying about every little undone chore." Though she was so tiny, Dame Dorcas seemed to be looking *down* at Mother! "John should help his father, but he should be given time to read, too," she said. "But now, ma'am, if you will be so kind as to excuse me, I shall return to my pupils. I wish you good morning. Come, John."

Mother looked very chapfallen, but she said nothing, for Dame Dorcas had already turned to the door. As she lifted the latch, she looked back.

"John Newbery," she said, "stop standing like a zany and get back to your lessons. I cannot abide an idle pupil. Let your recreation be lawful, brief, and seldom."

IT WAS a warm, sunny morning in late September. Everything looked gay, Henry Monk thought—the oak leaves dancing in the little wind, those puffy clouds up in the sky, even the tails of the scurrying rabbits.

Henry and John were trudging along the lane on their

CHAPTER *Three*

way to the fair at Waltham St. Lawrence. Henry felt so happy that he wanted to shout, to laugh, to whack at every bush with his stick. Races, gingerbread, ballad-singers, dancing on the green! The very thought was enough to make him burst out singing.

He began to bellow out "Johnny Armstrong" loud and clear; but he saw that John was staring at him in a funny sort of way. Henry's freckled face went red right up to the roots of his bright red hair. He knew that his singing didn't please others as well as it pleased him. His own father said he sang like a foghorn.

"I won't sing no more," he said guiltily.

"Eh? What did you say, Henry?"

Something must be amiss with John. He hadn't said ten words since they started out, and they bound for the fair!

"Cat got your tongue?" Henry asked.

"I was just thinking. Henry, do you suppose your uncle would let me have the loan of *Pilgrim's Progress?*"

"Like as not."

Henry's uncle was innkeeper in Waltham St. Lawrence and a very famous man. He got two London newspapers by post every week and had been known to spend all of a guinea on a parcel of books.

"I'll rub down his horse for a fortnight to pay for the

loan." John's breath seemed to be coming very hard and fast.

Henry shot John an uneasy look. All this to-do over a book! John had always seemed just like other boys, and he was a good hand at any game; but lately he'd been as if a spell was on him. And Dame Dorcas said he was like to write books himself some day! The very notion was fair creepy. Johnny, whom he'd known all his life! Henry scowled and gave a bush an extra big whack with his stick. What he'd best do was turn the talk, and quick.

"I made Molly a lamb out of some fir cones," Henry said. "Fair tickled, she was." Henry shook his curly red head and grinned; he was very fond of his little sister. "Molly's a queer one; dresses her doll in a hollyhock gown and lays it under a quilt of mullein leaves. When I'm growed, I'm going to have ten children, all like her."

"Henry, how does one get more books to read? Scarce as hens' teeth, they are. I've read every single one in Dame Dorcas's house, and 'most all your uncle owns."

"You must be witched." Henry sounded really worried. "Fretting so over old brown books. Folks will think you're loony if you keep on like this. It isn't natural-like."

"Old brown books, indeed! They'd be dressed in scarlet and gold, some of them, if the outside showed what the inside was like." John stopped suddenly, and a surprised look came

29

over his face. Then he broke out in a broad grin and clapped his hand on his thigh. "That's it! It's no matter for such as know the value of books, but all the little chapbooks of Jack the Giant Killer and such ought to be done up with pretty gilt covers without and pictures within, especially to get folks started. I warrant you'd not turn up your nose at books if they were decorated as fine as gingerbread at the fair!"

Henry laughed. "Not if they were as good to eat."

"But they *are* good." John was quite serious again. "Not to eat, but do you know what books are, Henry? They are windows that let folks see out—out on the whole world."

"Talk sense!"

"Things like those American colonies that have red Indians walking along the streets and bears and tigers and buffaloes roaring in the woods. And London and the King!" John's eyes were gleaming. "There are fairs in London that would turn up their noses at our Waltham one. They show strange animals you wouldn't believe in. There's one called a mocock with a snout like a cat and a body like a monkey. It comes all the way from the East Indies."

"It does?" Henry was gaping.

"Yes, it does. Henry, I'm going to tell you a secret; one of these days I'm *going* to London. I'll see the Lord Mayor in his golden coach and all the famous men that write books, too.

30

There are all the books in the world in London!"

Now, that was a bit thick. Henry's face was stern when he turned to John. Someone ought to talk sense to him.

"Your wits are wandering," he said bluntly. "What you're going to do is stay here, same as me, and hoe and harrow and feed the pigs and spool your mother's yarn and be a farmer. You'd best mind what your father says, too, or you'll get a bigger taste of the birch than you'll like."

"Henry, there's a thing I haven't told you yet. Mother acts different since she had that talk with Dame Dorcas. Afore then, if I sneaked off to read, she sent me to bed without any supper; but today when I told her I was going to borrow another book from your uncle, all she did was just nod her head."

"But how about your father, John?"

"He was smoking his pipe, and all he said was, 'Depend on your finger tips, lad, rather than your friends.'"

"What I say is, pigs can't fly!" Henry gave a loud snort and broke into a run. "Come on, come on," he shouted over his shoulder, "or like as not we'll miss the racing."

31

I<small>N</small> A FEW moments the boys came out on the
highway. They could see the town from here. A great oak
gateway stood there in front of them, and to one side was Castle
Acres, with what was left of the old Roman fort. They could
see the church, the pound for stray animals, guarded by great

CHAPTER *Four*

oak trees, and the little shops on the green. There was the water mill, and White Horse Inn! Eyes shining, the boys ran through the gateway and joined the merry holiday throng on the green.

There were people everywhere: milling around the green, bargaining for trinkets at the gaily decorated booths, and hurrying off to the downs where the races were to be run off. The same old Waltham St. Lawrence they knew and loved; only today it was just as if it had on new clothes. The sounds were different. There was no ring of hammer on anvil, no creak of the old mill wheel; the church bells were pealing out, flags were whipping, folks were shouting. It was a holiday, and everyone was out to make merry.

There was a coach just drawn up before the inn, and the boys stared open-mouthed at two ladies in bright-colored cloaks and befeathered hats, at a man in a fine coat with brass buttons. A postilion began to water the horses at the trough, and Mistress Betty hurried out of the inn, bobbing her head and curtsying. From the open door came the savory smell of roasting goose, and you could hear the merry sounds of tankards banging in the taproom, of voices laughing and singing.

John darted toward the inn. "I must stop and see your uncle."

"You lost your wits?" Henry caught John's sleeve; he

33

spoke impatiently. "Uncle is bound to be at the downs. The strawberry mare is in the race."

John nodded; what a silly goose he was to have forgotten that! They broke into a run, and presently there were the downs, stretching away before them. They stopped a moment to catch their breath and stare. A sight to make your heart fair jump. Bunting and flags on scaffolding; rows of booths all trimmed out with flowers and filled with sweets, fruits, toys, and baubles. Someone was playing a flute—must be old Peg Top—and there were children dancing to the tune. Lowing cattle and baaing sheep, penned in by hurdles, added to the noise, and you could hear farmers and drovers haggling over them.

John and Henry were shoving a way through the crowd when a friendly booming voice hailed them: "Well, bless me, if it isn't my own nephew and Robert Newbery's lad!"

"Good morning to you, Uncle."

"Good day, sir." John's head was bobbing. "A fine morning."

"How fares the reading, John?" The stout, ruddy-faced man laid an affectionate hand on his shoulder.

"Middling good, sir. Books are precious hard to come by."

"Drat it! Old books again!" said Henry. "Uncle, when

will they have the wrestling? I'll warrant Ned Downing will
lay that lad from Kent in the dust afore he can say Jack Robinson."

"The wrestling is over, Henry, and so are the foot races;
but you've still time a-plenty for the horses. You know my
Maggie will run?"

"O' course I do, and let's be off." Henry was jumping up
and down in his excitement.

"Mr. Monk, durst I ask for the loan of *Pilgrim's Progress?*"
said John eagerly. "I promise to take mortal good care of it."

"Wasting time about books when the race is going to
start!" Henry was tugging at his uncle's sleeve. "I'm fair
bursting to see it."

The innkeeper and John were laughing as they turned towards the long open space, already ringed with people, where
the race was to be run. A few minutes, and John had forgotten
all about books. He was swept into the excitement of that
scene. Already the horses were being lined up at the starting
line. They were pawing the grass, rearing, and prancing. The
riders held them in with tight reins, speaking soothing words,
patting their glossy necks. Then there came the sound of a
pistol; they were off!

It was fair thrilling, John thought. Folks were screaming
for their favorites; they were waving neckerchiefs, hopping

from one leg to another. The horses seemed to know what was afoot, to see those excited faces, to hear the shouts, for their hoofs were hardly touching the ground. Scarcely breathing,

36

John watched as the beautiful swift bodies sped past the spot where he stood, manes flying. One chestnut stumbled and went down on its haunches, but the next moment it had bounded to its feet and was running again. The race was three times around the course, and now the horses were in the home stretch. John could see the judges leaning forward, flags on long sticks in their hands.

"Uncle, it's Maggie! She's taken the lead."

As he spoke, Henry clutched his uncle's arm. His eyes were popping out of his head, his red curls stood on end, his body strained towards the course. Yes, the strawberry mare *was* inching ahead.

"Come on, Maggie, come on! Give them a taste of your dust." The innkeeper was screaming the words, both arms outstretched as if he were begging her to win.

But now the great black, running just behind the mare, was gaining. He was abreast of Maggie, he was a half head in the lead. A moaning sound was coming from the innkeeper's throat. Henry's fingers were clutching his hair. John felt as if he were out there trying to *shove* on the strawberry mare. And it almost seemed as if Maggie heard those three pleading voices, saw her owner's outflung arms, for suddenly she tossed up her head, she gave a mighty sprint, and she had broken away from the black horse. Maggie was over the finish line first!

37

Trembling with pride, Henry led the winner off to her stable. John and the beaming innkeeper followed, the latter bowing and waving to his friends in the crowd. And, as if something had suddenly tapped on his heart, John had the queerest feeling. How could he ever have thought he would some day leave Waltham St. Lawrence and a farmer's life? Why, it wouldn't be very long before *he* had a strawberry roan, before *he* won races, before Parson handed *him* a prize for the year's best crops. He thought of those blooming hedgerows, of the way the climbing roses covered the cottage walls, how the kitchen smelled after Mother had baked bread. He remembered the way the larks rose of a morning, with quivers full of song, the stretch of bluebells in front of Dame Dorcas's school, the times he and Henry went fishing.

John gave his head a sharp shake. No, he was going to be a farmer, just like Father. When they were growed, he and Henry would lean over the fence and talk about barley crops and lambs, about whether or not there'd be rain tomorrow. He couldn't leave here, not ever.

John felt this way even more strongly in the inn stables, for the innkeeper was a notable dealer in fine horseflesh and supplied the stables of all the gentlemen round about. He felt it while Master Monk was standing treat to dinner at the inn, with roast goose and suet and molasses pudding. But then they were finished, and the innkeeper led them through the inn parlor to his own private room behind. Master Monk was smiling as he pulled down a rather shabby-looking book from the well-filled shelf.

"Here is *Pilgrim's Progress*, John," he said. "Parson would look down his nose at it, for it was writ by a Dissenter, but 'tis a good religious book for all that, and a fine lively tale."

"Sir, I—I thank you."

"If old John Bunyan could but see your face now, lad, he'd think that all the sweat and toil of writing a book was well worth it. But look 'ee here." The innkeeper had turned back to the shelves. "I have half a mind to let you read this one, too. 'Tis a new-writ book, all about the sights and sounds of London Town." Master Monk rammed a finger against John's ribs and chuckled. "Wait till you read about the shipping anchored in the Thames! Full-rigged ships that have sailed all the seven seas, and goods from every country in the world. And that bit about the fogs they have, so thick the drums are beat to show the watermen the way to shore. I'll wager my Maggie against a ha'penny, lad, that book will so fire you that you needs must be a roamer and see it all for yourself."

That tapping at his heart, that feeling that he could never leave home, had gone; John had never felt it. Walking back with Henry an hour later, he didn't see a single heather blos-

39

som, a solitary scampering rabbit.   He was in London Town, looking at a river thick with ships; he was staring breathless at a gold coach, drawn by six horses, that went galloping by with the King himself inside it.

*I*T WAS Twelfth Night, and John was staying at his grandparents' farm for the holidays. They were growing old, and often John or his brother came to help with the work. The raftered room was still decked with holly and mistletoe. Christmas in England in those days did not end with

41

CHAPTER *Five*

December twenty-fifth; one called the twelve days following "in the Christmas"; one spoke about a thing happening "before Christmas was out."

Tomorrow John, with the other children of the neighborhood, would put Twelfth Night cakes by the hedgerow for the Three Kings. Legend said that they always passed through England on their journey, and it warmed their hearts to catch sight of the cakes made in the shape of star, moon, and camel. Of course John had never seen the travelers, though every year he hid for a whole hour near the hedgerow, listening for the sound of hoofs. But it did not matter; just the thought of those riders moving through the cold moonlight was enough to make you shiver with excitement.

Today had been a great day too. John had gone with his grandfather and the neighbors to wassail the old apple trees. They had made a circle, joined hands, and sung this song:

> "To blow well and to bear well,
>   And so merry let us be,
>   And every man drink up his cup,
>   And health to the old apple tree."

Then they lifted their tankards of wassail and drank. John had had to giggle when he saw a neighbor's lad pin a farmer's coat tail to that of another man; the men couldn't say a word, because it was a Twelfth Night custom. Again they all filled the pewter tankards from the great bowl, and they called in a shout, "Apples now! Hatfuls, cupfuls, bushels, bagfuls, little heaps under the stairs! Hip, hip, hooroo!" They stamped their feet to a dancy tune, and a gun was fired off. Then they trudged back to the house, and Granny and her friends served the Twelfth Day supper. There was roast beef, roast goose, mince pies, plum porridge, and, to end the feast, more big slices of the Twelfth Day cakes.

Now John and the others were all sitting around a roaring fire, ready to "see Christmas out." And presently Grandfather came marching in very proudly, bearing the wassail bowl. Everyone drank one last time to the dying Christmas and to the new year ahead. And then the men began pulling down the holly and mistletoe and piling them on the fire. A great rushing flame leapt up, sweet-smelling as heather; it roared up the stone chimney. Slowly the logs crumbled to red embers. The guests stood up. They began to gather their greatcoats and shawls. They shouted a good-by.

Lying in bed that night, warm and drowsy, filled with food, John heard the door open and saw Granny come in. She was tall and wizened, and her hair was very white under her mobcap. She had a snowy kerchief crossed over her bodice and a red woolen skirt with panniers. Now she put down the candle and drew up a chair to the bed. John was always a bit frightened of Granny; she was very stern and straight-lipped and didn't often smile. But he knew she was kind. Wasn't she always doing something for sick folks, nursing an ailing lamb or colt, seeing that her household was fed and cared for?

"You look a mite peakèd tonight, child. You have a rash on your face, too. How do you feel?"

"Oh, Granny, I'm as well as well." John was cringing away, trying to pull the quilt over his head. Brr! Granny's remedies!

"I know cheese from chalk, and don't you be forgetting that, my lad. If there be sign of rash on your face tomorrow, I shall spread a paste of toads' warts on it."

"No, Granny. *Please*, no."

"You have been too much cosseted, John. Open your mouth. Ah, I might have knowed it! You failed to rub your teeth with the sage leaf. My good mother always used to say, 'If you'd keep your teeth from rot or aching, rub them well with sage.' "

"Dame Dorcas says in London they use a brush to scrape their teeth with."

"A brush! Hoity toity! What is the world coming to?"

"Maybe there are good new ways there that we don't know anything about, Granny." John spoke a little saucily, and his grandmother bridled.

"Mind your manners, boy. A child's speech should be godly and respectful. His duty is to fear God, obey his elders, and honor the King."

"The King, Granny? Tell me about the time your mother

45

danced for the King." John knew she liked talking about "the old King," and if only he could get her to talk about him now, she might forget all about those cures.

"And prithee, why should I not?" Granny gave her head a toss. "A monstrous fine monarch was King Charles; we've had none like him since."

"Granny, tell me again about those Twelfth Night revels he used to hold."

She gave John a suspicious look. She knew what he was trying to do—pull the wool over her eyes, get the talk away from that toad's paste. But there was a side to Granny that loved nothing so well as a palaver about the good old days. She gave a sniff, but she had hitched her chair closer to the bed, and her blue eyes sparkled.

"My mother oft told me about that great masquerade that His Majesty held on Twelfth Night. True, there'd be lords and ladies in wondrous silks and velvets, but on this night the poor folks was invited, too. All the dancers wore masks on their faces. Clad in a gown trimmed with holly and mistletoe, my mother danced right afore King Charles himself, and he sitting right there on his golden throne."

"And he clapped his hands!"

"He clapped his hands, and he up and poured her a goblet of wassail straight out of the royal bowl itself."

46

"Then what happened?" John gave a soft sigh as he propped himself upon his elbow. He could fair see the scene.

"He went to the royal chapel, and two courtiers marched with him, bearing in a bag of scarlet and gold lace the gifts of the Wise Men to the Babe Jesus. I hear tell how even to this very day the kings keep up the custom."

"It must be a fearful exciting thing to be King, Granny. Think of him eating peacock tongues on a silver salver, with fine music playing—"

"Music, yes," Granny broke in eagerly. " 'Pears like all kings do have an amazing fondness for it, all the way down from Old King Cole to—"

"King Cole! Who was he?" John could name all the kings of England from William the Conqueror to George the First, but never once had he heard tell of this one.

"He is in a song, one my own granny used to sing to me. 'Pears like those old songs and rhymes and riddles are older than time itself. Fair handed down through the years, like my grandmother's bed warmer. I'll warrant there be hundreds of them."

"Hundreds?" John was staring at her. "You'd think someone would be setting them betwixt the covers of a book. Seems like folks' memories can get holes in them at times, and then the rhymes would be forgot."

47

"Fiddle-de-dee! Why waste time over cradle songs?" Granny stopped and gave a little start. She was pointing at the hearth. "If that poker hasn't slipped down and formed a cross against the bars! 'Tis a good sign, John. It means no witch durst come nigh the house for a twelvemonth." Granny took the candle and stood up. " 'Tis high time you get to sleep, now. What with all those rich victuals and this poke o' words I've been giving you, I'm fearing you'll be having wild dreams tonight."

"Granny, please don't go afore you sing me 'Old King Cole.' "

She nodded and sang the song for him. Then she tucked him in and wished him good night, standing beside the bed to say softly the old prayer:

"Matthew, Mark, Luke, and John,
 Bless the bed that thee lies on."

Just as Granny had foretold, John *did* have dreams that night. He dreamt that he stood in a great court where King Cole sat upon a golden throne, his scepter in his hand. He gave a shout and called for his fiddlers three; only what they brought him was not fiddles, but platters heaped with roast goose and plum porridge.

The dream woke John, and for a while he lay there in the

bright moonlight, his eyes wide open.   He was saying over and over to himself the words of Granny's song:

"Old King Cole was a merry old soul,
   And a merry old soul was he.
   He called for his pipe,
   He called for his bowl,
   And he called for his fiddlers three.

"Every fiddler, he had a fiddle,
   And a very fine fiddle had he;
   'Twee tweedle-dee, tweedle-dee,' went the fiddlers.
   Oh, there's none so rare
   As can compare
   With King Cole and his fiddlers three."

D~AME~ Dorcas spooned red currant jam onto a
crumpet, filled a mug with milk, and handed both to her visitor.

"Fill up, lad," she said, "and if you crave more, do not fear
to ask. 'Tis not every day that a boy observes his thirteenth
birthday."

CHAPTER *Six*

"I thank you, ma'am," John said, blushing.

He was sitting up straight as a ramrod on the three-legged chair. His threadbare smock was very clean; his face shone with soap and water. It was not every day that a boy observed *any* birthday in Dame Dorcas's parlor. All afternoon he had been wondering why she had invited him. It couldn't be just because he had brought her that basket of wild strawberries last week. No, the reason must be that he had been helping teach the younger children all this spring.

"I'll warrant you've been cudgeling your brains as to why I bid you come here, lad."

"Eh?" John gave such a start that he almost spilled his milk. Dame could see right inside a body's thoughts!

" 'Twas for two reasons, John: I can teach you nothing more, and I wish to tell you about a man in Reading, a printer and publisher."

He would be leaving school. John had known that it would happen soon, and now it *was* happening. He looked desperately around the room. He had come to love everything here—the stuffed owl whose eyes followed you no matter where you sat, the corner cupboard with blue and white china in it, and above all, those rows of books, books that he had bor-rowed and read, one after another.

"Dame, if you please," he said hoarsely, "I couldn't bear

51

to leave school—or you." John's fingers, setting down the mug, were unsteady. "If you could only see your way to letting me stay, I'd learn them—"

"*Teach* them, you mean, John."

"Yes, ma'am. I'd teach the older boys and girls their reading and counting, as well as the little ones—I'm fair at sums now, and I do know by heart the names of all the cities in England—and I'd promise to scrub the floor and bring in wood for the fire."

Dame Dorcas cleared her throat busily. A fellow would almost think she was finding it hard to speak. Then she lifted her chin.

"No, John Newbery," she said, "there's an end on it. I am not a learned woman. I have but a smattering of history and geography, and I have taught you all I know—maybe a smidgeon *more* than I know." Dame Dorcas wasn't looking at John now, and there were two red spots on her cheeks. "Those lines of Caesar—I'm not even sure that I pronounced them right."

"I liked the way you spoke them."

"Pish! Don't you be trying to flatter an old woman." Dame Dorcas tucked a strand of hair under her mobcap. "Parson says that confession is good for the soul; well, when I told you there are only three civilized lands in the world besides

England—France, Italy, and the Low Countries—I was mistaken. It would seem there is learning, too, in the American Colonies. I read as much in a book that Master Monk lent me last week. I am mortified, lad, to have misled you."

"You mean they have book learning there, too? How is it possible with all those bears and buffaloes and wolves roaming the place, and red Indians tomahawking folks? Henry's uncle, the one that's a sailor, sent him a letter from a town name of Boston and said the snow there was five feet high. I'd give a pretty to see those Colonies."

"All in good time, lad, all in good time. For a boy thirteen years of age, you already know a deal." Dame Dorcas looked at John gravely and said slowly, "John Newbery, are you still minded some day to write books?"

"I'm not one to shilly-shally. You know that, ma'am."

"I believe the thing must be in your blood, lad. One of your forefathers, Humphry Newbery, a man of learning, was a barrister in Lincoln's Inn a hundred years ago, and Ralph Newbery published books in Queen Elizabeth's day. You must have heard he left a sum of money to our town, to be distributed every Christmas to the needy poor." Dame Dorcas smiled at John and rubbed her spectacles on her apron. "Certain it is that booklearning seems to be natural to one John Newbery."

Now she was biting on one of her ear rims, and John, suddenly feeling quite bold, just as if he were talking to Henry, said, "One of these days, Dame Dorcas, I'm going to invent a pair of spectacles for you. One ear piece will be coated with peppermint, and the other with licorice. Then you will have pleasure sucking them."

"Mercy me!" Dame Dorcas was laughing merrily. "Just you make those rims out of sugarplums, and upon my word, I'll buy them of you." She didn't sound at all like a teacher now. Then she stopped laughing. Her face seemed to be working in a queer way, and when she spoke, her words sounded as if they had stuck in her throat. "Dear lad," she said, "how ever will I get on without you?"

"I'll miss you sorely, too." He'd best not look at her. Why, it was almost as if she were crying.

"What would you say, John," she had swallowed hard, and now she sounded like a teacher again, "what would you say if I gave you an introduction in a year or two to William Carnan?"

"William Carnan? Who is he?"

"A printer in Reading and a man held in high esteem. He publishes the oldest newspaper in Berkshire. Perhaps you could keep his ledger books. He could teach you the way to be a printer."

"Learn the way to be a printer! Keep books!" John's

54

heart was thumping. "It's like a fine dream a body has at night."

"I always hold the best part of a dream is the waking up, because then you can busy yourself making it come true. Fortune favors the brave, John Newbery, and don't you be forgetting it.

"You help your father now the best you can, but every spare moment you can find, you beg or borrow every book you can from Master Monk and Parson and the Squire. If you do, I'll warrant you'll find yourself setting out over the miles for Reading before you know it."

"Dame, I—" But John couldn't say any more.

"One crosses a delicious plain to come to Reading, lad. It lies on the highway betwixt Bristol and London, and is part circled by the River Thames. Follow that river and one comes straight to—"

"To London!" John was on his feet, shouting the words. "Where the King is and the Tower where they keep the lions and St. Paul's and St. Paul's Churchyard where the booksellers shops are!"

"Bless me, boy, your eyes are fair shooting sparks!"

"Dame, do you know what I'm going to do? See everything in England with my own two eyes."

"London alone is a school where a body learns new ways."

Dame Dorcas's eyes were almost as bright as John's. "New ways to travel with his thoughts as well as his legs."

"Dame," John's voice was suddenly shy, "do you reckon that if one day a country bumpkin should open a bookshop there, the famous writers of London would—would maybe come inside?"

"Aye, lad, I reckon as much."

"I'd work from sunup to sunset to learn my trade—London would want no truck with a lout, I'll warrant." John's glance was a thousand miles away. "Then," he said, "when I had some coins to jingle in my pocket, I'd travel a bit before I went up to London. I'd not waste those hours either, Dame, a-counting steeples. I'd keep a memorandum book and jot down all I saw and heard. Seems like a writing man must have something to put in his books."

"Seems like."

At that moment John Newbery looked so shining-eyed that Dame Dorcas had all she could do not to throw her arms about him. "You are a dear lad," she said. "Just you keep at that studying and reading."

"That I do now. Mother says that I read every which way; on my stomach, my back, and my side, in candlelight, firelight, and the light of the stars."

"And what does your father say, John?"

"He says naught, but he lets me read mornings from five to six—a good time, too, seeing as the hedgerows smell so sweet then. I need not do the milking, either; my brother Bob attends to that." John stopped; he was twisting his fingers and looking down. He said softly, "Dame, it has all been your doing."

"Fiddle-de-dee! I have done naught, lad."

"And I've something else to say. I have small liking for poverty; it nags at a body. I am going to be prudent and saving. When I am a man of means, I'll buy my mother a silken gown, and my father shoes with silver buckles. For you, Dame, I—I'll build a new school, one fair bulging with beautiful new books."

"Write or sell books, John." Her voice sounded queer again, as if the words wouldn't come out right. "Either will be return enough for anything I have done."

"I thank you for everything, ma'am." There was a prickling feeling behind John's eyes, and he blinked quickly. "But now I must bid you good day. Squire he promised me the loan of a history of England if I would help mow his lower meadow." John gave a little laugh. "Dame, he said a monstrous queer thing when I told him how I wanted some day to go to London. He said, 'Berkshire has a name for being skittish; it is forever heaving out its sons to London Town.'"

57

THE types are in this case, John, as well you know from keeping them so well sorted. Try setting this last line in the composing stick. There's your first step. Careful! There mustn't be any pye."

"Pye? I don't rightly know what it is, Mr. Carnan."

CHAPTER *Seven*

"A page with confused letters, John." William Carnan laughed. " 'Tis not the same kind of pie my wife makes, with apple and clotted cream atop. If a printer uses too much ink, it is called sopping the ball, and you've heard me talk about a squabbled page. Well, that is when the letters in one line have slipped into another."

John nodded. "That makes it clear as day, sir," he said.

"Good. Then we'll proceed. The stick is full now, so you transfer it to this shallow tray—we call it a galley. . . . Hand me over that ball of string. That's it, lad. Wind it around the galley. See? A mite tighter; makes the type rigid. . . . Now lay it in the bed of the press, and ink it well. . . . Next thing is the proof impression. Why, your hands are shaking! Steady does it, boy."

"Now—now I read it over to look for mistakes, Mr. Carnan?"

"Right." The printer was looking over John's shoulder and beaming. "Upon my word! Not a single squabbled letter. Congratulations, lad. Apprentice John Newbery, you have come a long way towards being a printer."

There was a little silence while John read the galley proof intently. He was breathing hard; his forehead was wet. Wasn't he setting type for the very first time? His own line at the bottom of the galley looked just like all the others!

John had been living with Mr. and Mrs. Carnan for more than two years now. He had kept the books, run errands, carried material to and from Mr. Carnan's warehouse, and served as apprentice. He had been happy. His employer was a kind and friendly man. Mr. Carnan had taken an almost instant liking for the rosy-cheeked country boy, with his alert ways, his pleasant manners, his excellent penmanship. He didn't mind—in fact he encouraged it—that John spent all his free moments in studying. When Dame Dorcas had written, saying that the lad she was sending him wasn't cut out to be a farmer, she had been right; John was too eager to read, to find out all that was happening in the big world, ever to be content to harrow a field of oats.

William Carnan had managed to work up a fair business in the little market city, with his newspaper and printing shop. He saw that his apprentice was as industrious and ambitious as he was, and he liked nothing better than to give the lad "a leg up."

The printer was smiling now as he led John over to the big press.

"Now the type is safely locked in the form," he said, "we untie the string and set in narrow wedges of wood to fill it out. . . . Ah, that's it! Watch well, now; we are inserting clamps on two sides to keep the type firm." Mr. Carnan looked at his helper's tight, frowning face, and he grinned. "The fate of the whole world doesn't rest on you, lad. Calm down. . . . There, now you have put the form in the bed of the press, you proceed to ink it with this leather ball."

"Y-yes." John's sigh was so loud that even little Tom Carnan, playing with a top outside the door, must have heard it.

"Now for the paper—the best damask there is, do you notice? The best always pays in the end, John, and don't you ever forget the fact."

"No, sir." John's ink-smudged hand was pushing back his hair. "Let me do it! Let me do it myself! The frisket, 'tis the paper frame you set over the sheet of paper, to keep the margins clean-like? There, it is all spread smooth. And *I* did it."

"That's the spirit, John. There may be more ink on your face and fingers than there be on the type, but after all, smudges be a printer's trademark. . . . Now we're ready for the big job, lad. Lower that tympan, and press down the lever. A man-size task, running those levers; small wonder there's sweat pouring down your face. Well, seems like those farm jobs of yours gave you stout muscles; you'll soon get the hang of this. Pull out that sheet, and take a look at your handiwork."

Slowly, carefully, John obeyed. A sheet of printed words lay there before his eyes, with not a single smudge!

"I've done it," he whispered hoarsely. "I've done it, sir!"

"And a right workmanlike job it is, lad." William Carnan was putting an affectionate arm on John's shoulder. "It must be nigh on noon, though, so come out in the yard, and we'll munch our bread and cheese. I'll warrant there be a mint of questions you'll be wanting to ask me, soon as we've eaten."

A half hour later, John lay back on the grass, hands locked behind his head. It felt nice here in the garden. It was a day in early June, and the air was clean and sweet-scented. You could smell red clover and Mrs. Carnan's roses. In the distance the River Thames glinted blue and silver.

"Mr. Carnan," John said softly, "a body must need a heap of learning to be a printer. I would I knew more."

William Carnan nodded. "Printing, lad, is an exacting and honorable craft. A man could study all his life and still not know the half of it. Take just the way the metal is made ready for the type. Iron, antimony, and lead are first boiled in a great brick furnace. The workers must lay their ears near the ground to listen to that bubbling sound that tells them the mixture has cooked long enough. While the metal is cooling, the men are always given a half pint of sack with salad oil, to restore their spirits; 'tis a grueling task they have. I ought to know; I used to watch my own father laboring over that furnace when I was a boy."

"But to print a fair page makes all that work worth while."

"That it does, lad. I like to muse on the pleasure I am bringing people when I am folding those sheets and sewing the edges. Bless me, if a book doesn't hold the hopes and fears and dreams of men!"

"I know." John's head jerked excitedly. "Mr. Carnan, when I brought the lever on that paper just now, I thought to myself, it is like an executioner's ax, chopping off folks' ignorance."

Mr. Carnan laughed. "I must remember that one."

"Were you a young boy when you first learned how to print?" John asked respectfully.

"Yes, John. I began as a journeyman printer, complete with composing iron, shears, sponge, bodkin to correct the letters, packthread, and a sliding box to hold the type. I vow I felt as important as the Lord Mayor of London."

"How long will it take me to be a journeyman, Mr. Carnan?"

"But a year or more, lad, if you keep on doing as well as you are now. You are honest and diligent, and you love the printed word. Small chance *you* will end as a smout."

"A smout, sir?"

"A compositor or pressman only employed now and then. It is ill taste to heap praise on myself, but you know, John, you fell on luck when you came to work with me. Most printers hold that they should pay their apprentices nothing while they are learning."

"But why not?" John was thinking anxiously of that growing pile of coins in a leather pouch under his mattress. With them, some day, he was planning, hoping, to travel about England before he went to London.

"They have the notion that a lad who has served half his time and is paid for it is apt to give himself the airs of a journey-man. If he is not given his papers, he will spread the word that his master is a cruel man."

"You have been proper good to me, sir," John said very low. "Where would I be today if Dame Dorcas hadn't sent me to you?"

"Faith, lad, the shoe's on the other foot. *I* am the fortunate one to have you as my apprentice. I am a forthright man, and I shall speak frankly; you are a born printer, John."

John's eyes shone. "I mean to be as good a one as I can. And sir, you will maybe laugh, me being a country lout with small learning, but it is my hope one day to have my shop in London and sell my books to the great ones there."

"Aye, lad, and why not a man-sized dream while you be dreaming? I warrant that one day London will be glad to have you and your shop."

THE leaded window shone in the August sun-
light; the rows of books gleamed. The oak sign with the
legend, THE BIBLE AND SUN, rocked lazily in a little breeze.
Over the doorway, in a niche, was a carved figure of a man
reading. It was August, 1745; it was a corner of St. Paul's

65

CHAPTER *Eight*

Churchyard. John Newbery had opened his bookshop in London. John Newbery, thirty-two years old this very year.

It wasn't possible, John was thinking, that he could be the same person who once sat in Dame Dorcas's little parlor and talked about being a printer some far-off day. His clothes then had been shabby and poor, and now what was he wearing? The finest of broadcloth coats and breeches, and the best of linen.

All the things that had happened since that afternoon! As if they were scenes in a penny peep show, he seemed to be seeing them now. The happy, busy years in William Carnan's shop, where he set type, read proof, and kept the accounts. . . . The sad day when William died—it was in 1737—and then the discovery that he had left his business divided between his brother and his "faithful friend, John Newbery.". . . John running the newspaper, the printing shop, and a store that sold books, stationery, medicine, haberdashery, and cutlery. . . . John Newbery actually a publisher!

He was remembering other things, too. The day he married Mary, William's widow, and became the stepfather of her children. . . . The birth of his own little daughter. . . . That long trip he made, going from one famous city to another, to London, Leicester, Lincoln, and Sheffield. That memorandum book he kept about his travels, one filled with

66

notes about a fishskin boat come all the way from Greenland, a ducking stool to cure scolding wives, and ideas for books to print and names of books to read. . . . His return to Reading. . . . A son, John, born to him. Later another son whom they called Francis. . . . But all through the years, one thought, one dream: London!

And now he was there. Now he had his shop at the corner of St. Paul's Churchyard.

London! How he loved it, loved everything about it. All the sights. The shops—milliners, pewterers, drapers, confectioners, coffee houses, oyster shops, raffle shops. Oh, but best of all, the bookshops! St. Paul's Churchyard was surrounded with them. Books seemed to belong to the place, to the great stone church that Sir Christopher Wren had built on Ludgate Hill, and to all the little streets with religious names from the time of the medieval cathedral—to Paternoster Row, Amen Court, and Creed Lane.

Then the people everywhere! Merchants, porters, hurrying footmen, swaggering beaux, women and children. Boys and girls trundling hoops, playing hide and seek, dodging horses' hoofs, pressing their noses against the windows of sweet shops, selling their wares. A body could never have a single dull moment, John thought, if he lived in London Town.

People and sights, yes, but the *sounds!* Cries of chimney

sweeps: "Maids, shall I sweep your chimneys high?". . . Fish-
wives' shrill voices: "Oy, oy, lobsters good and cheap, crabs,
sprats!". . . The *tink*, *tink*, *tink* of the tinker's bell. . . .

The merry call of the peep show man. . . . Children calling "Muffins, Oh! Crumpets, Oh! Come buy, come buy of me. Muffins and crumpets for breakfast or tea.". . . Men selling ink, flowers, kidney pies. To walk along the streets of London Town was just like being at the Fair every single day of the year.

John smiled to himself. Why, if he didn't even like the smells! Meat, melting tallow, dogs, horses, the scents from pastry and sweet shops. Of course, the gutter that ran down the middle of the street was a bit foul, what with the refuse and all, and some folks were a mite shiftless, the way they left the crows and dogs to clean up their messes. One of these fine days, though, the Lord Mayor would see to it that the streets were better cleaned. John shook his head; anyone would think he was ten years old, and gazing at the sights of London for the first time in his life. Would he ever grow up?

Proudly his eyes went traveling around the pleasant room. There were rows of books on the shelves, gleaming in their new calf bindings. There were settles by the fire and painted benches set here and there; he wanted his customers to browse, not hurry. A fire was laid in the fireplace, all ready to be lit when a damp or gloomy day arrived. The pewter candle-sticks shone on the mantel. Oh, and that Chinese chest over in the corner, the one that held Dr. Hooper's Pills—held, too,

69

herb snuff, corn plasters, stomach lozenges! Its shelves would likely be empty within the week.

John walked briskly over to a bookcase and straightened a book that was pushed in too far. It was still quite early, not yet eight by the clock. The customers, though, would soon be coming. Hadn't he paid for a puff in the *General Evening Post* telling all about the shop's opening?

When young Tom Carnan, his stepson, came hurrying through the back door a minute later, he saw John standing frowning and drumming his fingers on the table.

"Tom, lad," he said, "I've a mind to add the *Canterbury Tales* to the shelves. A fine writer, Chaucer. You'd best run straight to Mr. Crane's shop and buy twelve of them. You know the place? The Red and Gold Flower Pot, next door to Widow Edwards' Coffee House over against the Bull and Gate. Here is the money."

"Yes, sir." Tom was beaming as he, too, stared about the shop, hands on his hips. "It is far and away the finest bookshop in all London, Father. If I were in your shoes, I'd fair burst with pride, I would."

"I admit I am, Tom, I admit I am." John sighed happily. "It has been a hard struggle, but well worth it. And I have been fortunate. Think of all those poor shopkeepers, back some eighty years ago, who had to start business all over again when the Great Fire of London destroyed their shops and all their goods. What a fearful loss!''

"But what a fine bonfire! Just like Guy Fawkes Day." Tom grinned boyishly and then was serious again. "Well, Father, your books are safe; and what a lot of them there are! 'Tis like a booklover's dream of heaven."

"Thank you, Tom. And don't think I am forgetting how you have helped me." John was looking affectionately at the tall young man. "Nor my wife's encouragement," he said. "That I will always treasure.

"But now, back to business. My master printer was complaining yesterday about that new composing iron. I'd best run back and see what ails it. Be on your way now, Tom. Oh, and one other thing: give no credit to any customer. I excuse myself from trusting any man by selling for naught but money on the counter. What money I have has been hard come by, nor have I forgot the bitter taste of poverty."

"Well, there is one customer that has already broken your rule, Father." Tom gave a mischievous grin. "Fair forced his way in, too, though the door was locked. It was yesterday, and he thundered on the pane with his cane until I was forced to open up. He demanded credit on a book, cool as a cucumber. You see, the man was Samuel Johnson!"

Samuel Johnson had been inside the shop! John's face

lighted up. The great ugly scholar with his shabby coat and his queer ways was getting a name as a notable author. Surely such a first customer would bring luck to any bookshop! John had already met him, and at times he was as touchy as a bear with a sore paw, at others gentle and kind.

To know this learned man! It was part of that dream that had come true. Going towards the door, John stopped to touch lovingly one book after another. Poetry, science, history, practical instructions, religious books! He had all of them here. And how stoutly bound were the ones he had printed himself! It was the way he had dreamt of making them away back in Reading. Nay, before that. Here was the *Little Pretty Pocket Book* that taught the alphabet in a song and gave directions for games. He had got that idea from the dull way he had to teach the little ones their letters in Dame Dorcas's school; he had even thought of the bright binding then.

Already John was making new plans. The *Little Pretty Pocket Book* was sold with a ball or pincushion for tuppence extra, and it could hardly have failed; but it was showing signs of such great success that John had ideas for many more like it. How he hoped the idea took on! He could imagine a whole series of little play books to allure children into learning their letters by way of diversion.

John put the little book down and almost burst out laughing. Why, I am already an author! And if I turn out one-tenth of the little books I have in mind, my collected works will be a noble sight! He was still chuckling as he opened the door. I am the luckiest man in all the world, he thought. The very luckiest.

IT WAS years later, a cold gray day in January. Outside the Bible and Sun bookshop, snow was falling steadily. The white flakes had done a better job than any crow or daw could have in cleaning up the dirt and litter on the streets; they had simply covered everything over.   On road and footpath,

74

CHAPTER *Nine*

on wheelbarrows and vendors' stands, the snow had spread a gleaming quilt.

Not a day to loiter on, though; too cold. Woolen scarfs knotted, coat collars high, people moved briskly to keep warm. It seemed to Melinda Pratt that her nurse was the only one who was not hurrying.

"Oh, please to make haste," she begged. "Mamma said that I might visit the bookshop today."

"If she hadn't been asleep when we left, and if she had but seen this pesky snow, she would never have allowed you to come out today," Nurse grumbled. "And anyway, whyever should a child not a month over eight years old want to put her nose inside a bookshop?"

"But it is a special shop, Nurse, with special books for children. Papa said that Mr. Samuel Johnson—the author of the great dictionary, you know—told him about the rows and rows of books there and about the owner, Mr. Newbery. My little pretty flowery-gilt books come from Mr. Newbery's Juvenile Library, and I have never been there. I shall be as safe as safe until you come back. Mr. Newbery knows a great many of Mamma's and Papa's friends."

"Fiddlesticks!" Nurse gave a sniff. "You ought to be at home embroidering your sampler, you ought."

"It will take you a great deal of time, won't it, to choose

those apricot tarts and the sugarplums at the confectioner's shop?" Now Melinda was looking down, and there was a guilty blush on her cheeks. "Mamma is *so* particular about tarts when they are for a dinner party."

Nurse shot Melinda a suspicious look. "Just what are you a-getting after?"

"N-nothing. It is just that I should like to see every single book there, and—and you will like the bookshop too. I shouldn't be surprised if there were a fireplace, and when you come, you could toast your toes there, Nurse."

"W-e-l-l—" Nurse was really glad of a chance for a good chat with the confectioner's wife, who had promised to show her a new tatting stitch the next time she came in. She cleared her throat and said sternly, "You must promise to mind your P's and Q's whilst I am away and not even put your head out-doors until I come. I shall watch you until you are inside."

"Yes, I promise."

As she spoke, Melinda had begun to mount the shallow steps that led into the bookshop. She turned a handle, a bell rang, and then she was inside. Goodness! What a queer and beautiful place! It seemed as if the shop were papered with books. There was even a little ladder to reach the highest ones. And what was inside that great Chinese chest? Oh, and look at the fire crackling in the grate!

"May I be of service, my dear?"

Melinda's head jerked up. It was a man speaking to her. He was quite short, he had very kind smiling eyes, and he wore a brown wig.

"I should like to know, sir, if you—if you sell book-worms?" she asked.

John Newbery blinked. He was looking at a tiny girl with great brown eyes and a little square chin. She had the soberest face that he had ever seen on a child.

"I did hear you aright?" John said. "I did hear you say bookworms?"

"Your ears, sir, were not deceiving you. You see, Mamma says that I am turning into a bookworm, but she must be mistaken. I thought that if I could just buy her a real one, she would see how wrong she is."

"Well, bless me! Bookworms are maggoty creatures that destroy books by eating their way through the pages. I'd not permit any such pest within a mile of *my* shop."

"Are they, indeed, sir? I think you must be Mr. New-bery, aren't you?"

Melinda had sat herself down very primly on one of the settles. Her buckled shoes were set close together, her mittened hands were folded in her lap. Her cheeks were pink, her eyes very bright and with very long lashes. A little maid pretty enough for even Joshua Reynolds' paintbrush.

"John Newbery, at your service, ma'am." He gave a bow. "And if you would know my opinion on that other matter, nobody could less resemble a bookworm than you do."

Now John was smiling. "But of course one's mother can never be wrong, so pray tell me, *do* you nibble on books?"

"Oh, no, sir, I do not." There was not even the tiniest of smiles on her lips; she was speaking very earnestly. "I dearly love all books. The only trouble is that I have read over and over all the ones I own."

"And just what are they about?" John sat down beside her.

"About learning to be good. I like my Juvenile Library books best of all because they are so pretty in their flowery covers and because they are little and they are never terrifying."

"Terrifying?"

"The ones about how children should always be in readiness to die frighten me. I wake up in the night, and Nurse is very angry."

"Your nurse!" John gave a start. "Where is your nurse? Does she know you are here? A child of your age alone on the streets. Good gracious! You might be kidnaped."

"There is small danger of that, sir. Nurse is in the confectioner's shop buying apricot tarts for Mamma's dinner party tonight. Mamma is very particular, too; so Nurse must take her time. Besides, I think that the confectioner's wife is showing her a tatting stitch."

79

"Ah, that is better. Pray, may I ask your name?"

"My name is Melinda Pratt, sir." The brown eyes looking at John were as grave as any grown-up person's. "May I say that if I had known I was going to meet you, I'd have worn my Sunday-best gown and my bonnet with the silk rosebuds. I expect you are a very famous person."

"The honor is entirely mine, and it grieves me that *I* have not on my best coat." John's eyes were twinkling. "Since we happen to be out of bookworms today, perhaps you will allow me to show you about the shop? Or would you rather browse alone?"

"Browse alone! But Mr. Newbery, you know nothing about me—if I am a good or bad child."

"Aren't you good, Melinda?" *Couldn't* he win a smile from her?

"Alas, no, sir, not very. I attend Dame Toosey's Select Seminary; so also does my cousin Dorothea. Every afternoon we are all supposed to tell Dame just how good or bad we have been. If one feels she has been very good, she says 'Five'; if just fairish, 'Four'; and when it's doubtful, she says 'Three.' Of course 'One' means you have been very, very naughty. Mr. Newbery, Dorothea's name is called right after mine, and she *always* says a higher number than mine. It is very provoking."

"I should think so! I do not believe that Dorothea is one

whit better than you are. I am sure you are very good indeed."

"Alas, no, sir. I often lose my temper and am quite unreasonable, and Nurse has to tell me to stand in the corner with my face to the wall."

"But you intend to be good, Melinda?"

"Oh, I do, Mr. Newbery!"

"Then that is enough for me." Didn't she ever laugh or play? As sweet as a blush rose, and yet such a little sobersides!

"Thank you, sir." Melinda was sending mouselike glances around the shop. "It is a very fine place you have here. I'd like full well to sell books myself."

John's lips twirked. "And I'd like full well to have you do it. Like seeing a garden pink a-bloom, it would be, in this sober old shop. Of course it would never do if you were to come on a bookworm and try to sell it—say to the famous Mr. Johnson. Wouldn't that old bear growl at you then!"

"I fear you are making fun of me, Mr. Newbery." She was blushing and looking down at the floor. "If Mr. Johnson does growl, I vow it is because he is hungry. At dinner parties, Papa says, he always eats a great deal, and eats it very fast. Mamma says she shivers when she looks at him. I shouldn't mind it, though."

"Is your mamma as pretty as you are, Melinda?"

"Oh, far, far prettier, sir! And she plays the harpsichord and goes to balls, and her headdress is full a yard high." There was a little catch in Melinda's voice. "I—I wish that I could see more of her, though, sir."

"But tell me, what do you do with yourself whilst your mother is so busy?" Poor mite! What a sober life she must lead! She ought to be bowling a hoop, romping, playing.

"Nurse and I go for walks. I have three china dolls, a ball, and a playhouse. I knit and sew seams, and I stitch my samplers, though at times I grow tired of them. One day, Mr. Newbery, I—I stitched in red yarn the words 'Melinda Pratt did this, and she hated every letter of it.'"

Again Melinda was looking down. "I was soundly whipped for that, but I still would rather read than sew. Only I feel sorry for the horrid example children—such dreadful things happen to them. And the good ones make me feel naughty. May I look at your Juvenile Library books now, Mr. Newbery?"

"Yes, indeed, and we shall try to find a story that will be much more entertaining than sewing a sampler."

"Oh, I am sure that will be very easy," said Melinda gravely, but she almost—not quite but almost—forgot her soberness as she looked at the shelves of little books bound in bright Dutch paper. "I know I shall like these books; they look so nice and cheerful."

Nice and cheerful! Suddenly John was pacing up and down the room. How cheerful *were* his books? He had remembered Dame Dorcas's school and how dreary that hornbook seemed to Molly Monk and little Rafe, and he had published bright little lesson books with pictures and been well pleased with himself. They had done well, too—he must be the first printer to make something of a specialty of books for children. But what a great deal more was still to do! And what a blind dolt he had been not to see it!

He looked anxiously at Melinda, who was earnestly poring over *The Circle of the Sciences*. There was nothing to make her smile in that. Perhaps T. Trapwit's jests in *Be Merry and Wise?* But that was so full of moral maxims and preachments! What this little girl needed was some regular nonsense, something as jolly as Granny's old songs.

John was standing at the window now, staring out unseeingly at the snowy street. Melinda Pratt had given him a great idea.

THE evening was as cold as the day had been, but John Newbery, scurrying along the street, coat-tails flying, hat awry, was not thinking about frost or darkness.

The linkboy, carrying his torch, was trotting on ahead. People who could help it seldom ventured out alone after dark

CHAPTER *Ten*

in London. The streets were so dark, so muddy, so full of ruts, and there was always the danger of footpads. Everyone was supposed to hang a lantern outside his door and keep a candle burning at the window, but the rule wasn't always obeyed.

On any other night, John's eyes would be darting everywhere, but now all his thoughts were set on where he was going, and he went quickly on.

"Eight o'clock, and a fine starlit night," called the night watchman, swinging his lantern and giving John a civil nod.

Now he had come to a poorer part of the city. Just ahead was a hill with dark houses and figures skulking down shadowy alleys. This was Ludgate Hill, and John was standing in Sea-Coal Lane. He paid the linkboy and began to climb a steep ladder made of flagstones and known as Breakneck Steps. Presently he stopped before a ramshackle building that had three of its windows bricked up, so that the owner wouldn't have to pay a window tax. John lifted the knocker.

A girl opened the door. She wore a tattered dress, there were smudges on her cheeks, and her hair fell in limp streaks; but she smiled from ear to ear when she saw it was John.

"Good evening, Tilly," he said. "Is Mr. Goldsmith in?"

"That he be, sir, and a-scribbling away for dear life."

"Then I'll go straight up."

"You'd best knock thrice, sir. 'Tis like rousing the dead

85

to make him notice when the writing fever has hold on him."

The steps were dark, steep and uncarpeted; there was a smell of damp, of cabbage, and of mice. John reached the garret and knocked on a battered old door. There was no answer. He knocked louder. Then someone shouted:

"Friend or bill collector? If friend, come in; if bill collector, turn around, and I hope you trip over the last three steps."

"Noll Goldsmith, open up, man. It is John Newbery."

"John, dear man, come in." The door was thrown wide open. "Sure, I was born to disoblige my friends. But a bookseller can make no complaint when he finds an author writing."

"It is good to see you, Noll."

John was smiling warmly as he sat down on a rickety chair. He was very fond of his extravagant Irish author. Oliver was rather short, he had a very ugly smallpox-pitted face, his clothes were shabby and untidy, and he had a slouching walk. For all that, his manner was so friendly, so happy-go-lucky, that John had taken a liking to him on first sight. The smallest thing made Noll happy. At this moment, if he wasn't rubbing hands and beaming, just as if John were the Lord Mayor himself, here to make a call!

John sighed, though, as he gazed around that old room under the eaves. What a home for a man who could write so well! On the stained walls, in Oliver's handwriting, were scrawled bits of descriptions. Stacks of old books were heaped on the floor, and the one strip of carpet was faded and moth-eaten. Poor fellow, John thought, pushing his quill so desperately hard just to earn bread and lodgings! The spotted shirt, the tattered breeches, the broken-down furniture! John shook his head. And the jobs that Oliver had had: pounding drugs, teaching school, playing his flute for supper and a lodging in France, even begging alms at convents in Italy.

"We are having a cold winter," John said.

"That chair is a bit wobbly. Stretch your carcass on the— er, yellow satin loveseat." Oliver was pointing to a sagging bed. "Oh, and pray help yourself to that platter of peacock tongues! I owe you an apology for the condition of the room, but as it happens, my valet is out, buying me a new flowered waistcoat."

"What a merry fool you are!" John had to laugh in spite of himself. "You can't deceive me, though; if your pockets weren't empty, you would never be driving that quill so hard."

"Empty!" Oliver spoke with a faint Irish accent. "I haven't two pennies to jingle together. I have been feeding on my own fat, as the bears do in wintertime in America."

"If it's a few guineas you need, man, why didn't you let me know?" John rose and handed Oliver three gold coins.

87

"Here, take these, and welcome. I'll put them on your account."

"Ah, thank you, John. You cannot lend me pennies, I know, because you've already tossed them all to the first beggar you saw."

"A fine one you are to talk about generosity." John laughed. "Anybody in need is welcome to your last farthing. The only trouble is that you give to beggars what is owing to your butcher and baker. Tell me, why have you not gone on with your study of medicine? You might have kept a decent roof over your head that way."

"I still at times prescribe remedies for my friends," Oliver said, smiling.

"Maybe you should keep them for your enemies." John laughed teasingly. But seeing that Oliver looked rather affronted, he added, "Nay, Doctor, I should say nothing against your judgment in medical matters, for I know you are a firm believer in Dr. James's Fever Powders."

"Which are to be had at John Newbery's shop at the corner of St. Paul's Churchyard," said Oliver drolly, quite forgetting his offended dignity. "Tell me, John, are you more a bookseller or a dealer in medicines?"

"You need not poke fun at my medicine business." John spoke a little testily. "They say the King's own physician has for sale a cure for mad dogs' bites. Nor do I think that you would turn up your nose if you could but see the coins pour into my till from the sale of those Fever Powders. They have even been found useful for cattle. And my other cordials and drugs have been of great service in many diseases."

"But I can think of something better to prescribe for starvation!" Oliver was grinning good-naturedly as he stumped across the room and out into the hall. Leaning over the broken bannister, he shouted, "Tilly! Tilly Winkles! Where *is* that girl? Ah, there you are! Skin round the corner, my dear, and get me a loaf of bread, a heel of cheese, and a bottle of Madeira. Oh, and, Tilly, buy yourself that red neckerchief if the shop is still open. But make haste; I'm starving."

Back in the room again, Oliver threw himself down on his chair, hands clasped behind his neck. "To what do I owe this visit, John?" he asked. "But first tell me about your family. How is Francis faring at school?"

"He will be off to Oxford soon. I can hardly believe it— a son of mine at Oxford University! Mary is well; she is almost a woman grown, now. You saw Frank in that Latin play at school, for I know he said you and Johnson and Garrick all came together and the other boys were almost too terrified to act."

Goldsmith laughed at the memory. "He was the funniest actor in the play, and Garrick himself praised his acting. If he is as good a tragedian as he is a comedian, he will soon provide Garrick with a rival."

"I hope he will take up the study of medicine. It is not so much play-acting as his fiddle that pulls him from his studies.

Johnson saw his fiddle hanging on the wall one day and gave him a piece of sound advice."

"And what was that?"

" 'Young man,' he said, in his downright fashion, 'give the fiddle to the first beggar man you meet, or you will never be a scholar.' "

"I fear that Johnson is very insensible to the power of music. But despite his own odd ways, he is great for solid sense. Francis Newbery will be no such scapegrace doctor as I, tramping France playing his flute—I mean his fiddle—for a lodging. When I was a lad, I conceived the idea of setting sail for the American colonies. Off I went on horseback with a few pounds in my tattered pockets. But a friend bade me to a party of pleasure, and if the ship did not sail an hour before I reached the dock! Well, out with it, John; I ought to be locked up in Bedlam as a lunatic."

"I look on it as good luck that America did not get you, Noll. One of these days you will be setting London agog with your books."

"Dear man, I love you for your trust in me." Oliver had bounded to his feet. "But if Tilly doesn't come soon with that food, I'll not live long enough to make good your prophecy. My stomach is rumbling like an empty keg."

"Oliver, I've a job for you that'll maybe help you keep

food in your mouth." John stopped, not quite knowing how to put his idea.

"More essays for the *British Magazine?*"

"No. Oliver, I know you like children."

"I sometimes give them a few tunes on my flute to buy a little quiet while I write, or show them a conjuring trick. They like my old songs." Oliver suddenly began to sing, "There was an old woman tossed in a blanket, seventeen times as high as the moon—"

John clutched his arm. "Noll," he shouted, "that's precisely the sort of thing I am searching for! Words that jump and frolic. Words that will make even that little sobersides, Melinda Pratt, plain have to laugh. Oliver, I need your help with my Juvenile Library!"

"My help? Am I to write A.B.C.'s for babes? What do I, a bachelor, know about the little dears? Nothing, I assure you. Nothing."

"Then you will learn. But this is not A.B.C.'s but a new idea. Oliver, I want stories that show a child not only how to be good, but how to be merry, as well. Crickets were made to cricket, and little boys and girls were made to laugh and be happy." John was waving his arms and pacing up and down. "You, Oliver, are going to write some of those stories to make children merry."

92

"John, you will lose every penny you own."

"No, I won't, Oliver. What do you say to a picture book of birds and beasts with rhymes for the different animals? 'Tommy Trip's History of Birds and Beasts.' That's it, Oliver —that's it!"

"Why, John—"

Oliver broke off. Tilly was coming clumping into the room, her arms bulging with packages. A bright red neckerchief was knotted about her throat.

"Here they be, sir," she chirruped. "A bit of a surprise throwed in, too. I saw some saustridges—mortal cheap, too— and two dried herrings going for next to nothing, being a bit high. You want me to clear a spot on your writing table, sir? It won't hurt to scatter the papers a bit? Just sort of scrawls, like, an't they?"

"Set it anywhere, so long as it is close to my gullet. I tell you, wench, I am starving."

"Yes, sir." Tilly was smiling from ear to ear. "Don't I look fair like a duchess in this red neckerchief? Oh, and Mother she sent up a plate for Master Newbery, and she says no extra charge for it, either, Master Goldsmith."

But Master Newbery was not even waiting for a single glance at plate or food; with a hurried, "Set to it tonight, Noll," he was gone.

93

FATHER! Father, where are you?" It was
Tom Carnan calling from the bookshop.

"In the back room," John answered. "Talking to Melinda."

Tom threw open the door. He was grinning. "Three

CHAPTER *Eleven*

urchins are here, sir, and they demand to see you on a matter of business. Won't take no for an answer, either."

"Then let them come in, let them come in. You know I never turn away a child."

Two minutes later John and Melinda blinked in astonishment. A girl and two boys had come in, and they were exactly the same size, they had exactly the same red hair.

"Please, sir, be you the owner?"

It was the little girl speaking. She had on a tattered black coat that was too large for her. A bonnet with a bright red feather that was propped up with a twig was set jauntily on her touseled hair. She was holding a large flat basket, and in it was a single muffin."

"I am, my dear," John said. "What may I do for you?" He was trying not to smile.

"These be my brothers." She jerked her head from one boy to the other. "One's Dave, one's Danny. I'm Deborah, but I be called Debby."

"A good morning to you all. Maybe you'll be kind enough to answer me a question?"

"Depends."

"Well, it is this; am I seeing triple?"

"Lor! Other folks get mixed up, too. We be triplets." Debby was tossing up her chin in a proud way. "One of these

95

days we may get asked to be put in Cox's Museum, 'cause triplets, they be scarce as hen's teeth."

"Not that we be *freaks*." Danny was speaking a bit worriedly. He wore a ragged greatcoat, torn breeches, and clogs.

"No, indeed!" John's eyes were twinkling as they traveled from Danny to Dave to Debby. All three of them had red hair, green eyes, and pointed chins. Alike as three peas in a pod, John thought. "Pray be seated," he said. "To what am I indebted for this call? You are looking for some book?"

"A book! Not us." Debby tossed her head, and the feather gave an emphatic bob. "We can't read. No need to; we be muffiners. What we want to know is, can we have 'sclusive rights to sell our muffins afront of your shop?"

"It's this way, sir," Dave explained; "there be so many children sticking their noses against your window that we have sold every single muffin in the basket, save—"

"Save this one here." Deborah held up the muffin.

"We kept *it* so you could see we do be honest-to-goodness muffiners," finished Danny.

"I see," said John politely. "And who challenges your 'sclusive rights?"

"Then you haven't seen her?" Dave was speaking now. "Name is Catsmeat Nan—sells scraps for cats—and she says she *owns* the front of your shop, she does."

"If only a devil's coach would come along and take a nip out of that Nan!" said Danny with a ferocious scowl.

"Please, what is a devil's coach? And does it really nip?" Melinda asked him, shivering a little.

"Nice velvet ribbons you got on your bonnet," Debby said. Her eyes were narrowing in a grown-up way; the way Mamma's did, Melinda thought, when she was buying a hat.

"Thank you," Melinda said.

"But don't you be giving yourself airs over them." Debby sniffed. "Take this feather of mine. 'Tis quality. Comes from Lady Lovelace's own trash box. Good as new, too." Debby nodded, and the feather nodded, too.

"Best mind your manners, Debby," Dave said. *He* thought Melinda's bonnet was pretty; he didn't want her feelings hurt, either. He explained politely, "A devil's coach, miss, is a cocktailed beetle, and if ever you saw one, your heart would fair stick to your ribs, it would."

"Oh, dear me!" Melinda said.

"What is your last name, children?" John asked.

"'Tis Monk. Master Henry Monk, our father was knowed as."

"Did you say *Henry Monk?*" John sprang to his feet. "Where did he hail from?"

"A town name of Waltham St. Lawrence," Debby said.

97

"Only he be dead. He took the smallpox, and they bled buckets o' blood from him, and he tried hard not to die, but he couldn't. Mother says so."

"My old friend Henry Monk dead! And you three are his children." Now John had put his hands on Debby's shoulders, and he spoke very sadly. "God love you, little dear—and Dave and Danny, too—'tis a sorry day on which I find you brought to this."

"Brought to this! What do you mean?" Debby pushed away John's hands and jumped back. She was glaring at him. "Let me tell you, Master Newbery, we be proud o' being muffiners. Why—why, *coaches* have stopped and bought our muffins, and the coachman ate them, too."

"And Catsmeat Nan, she be fair consumed with envy of us," Danny said.

" 'Tis only the truth Debby and Danny speak." Dave was banging his tin cup (the collections were kept in it) against the table to make everyone hear him. "No need to pity *us*. We be business folks. Nigh growed up, too."

"Tell me where you live, my dears," John said. "I must go see your mother and take her help. Why, I remember once Henry saying that when he was a man, he would have ten children, all like his little sister, Molly. And here you all are, looking instead like—like pixies." John smiled. " 'Tis a nippy sort of day, and calls for good hot food. So what would you say to going home with me and tasting some of my wife's cooking? I seem to remember her saying there would be roast beef today for dinner, with Yorkshire pudding."

"W-e-l-l, these *do* be our business hours, o' course," Debby said slowly.

"But all we had for breakfuss was a bowl o' cold porridge." Dave's lips were trembling.

"And roast beef, sort o' dripping gravy, do sound tasty-like," Danny said.

Tears prickled in John's eyes. Why, they were half starved, the poor mites! Shivering with cold, too. What was Melinda thinking about them, sitting there in her fine merino dress?

John turned and looked at her; he gave a little start. Melinda was staring at Debby and Dave and Danny with open admiration. She looked as if they had come straight out of a fairy tale!

MELINDA stood in the bookshop looking delightedly around her. It was several months since Mr. John had published those new books for children, but the sight of them on the shelves still made her catch her breath with pleasure. Row upon row of tiny, bright-covered books, and some

100

CHAPTER *Twelve*

of them for only a few pennies! *Poems for Children Three Foot High, Tommy Trip, Nurse Truelove's Christmas Box, The Philosophy of Tops and Balls.*

Melinda gave a soft little sigh. It was almost as if she were Mr. John's partner and the books were partly hers. Before Mr. John and Mr. Goldsmith and the other writers had even begun to write the books, Mr. John had talked and talked to her about what children liked.

Oh, dear, it would be almost like a dream, if it weren't for one thing! Mr. John said the books were not the way he wanted them to be. Because she didn't laugh when she read them and Debby, Dave, and Danny didn't even want to listen to them being read, he thought that there was something wrong with them.

Of course, he was right about the Monks. Hadn't she been reading them the stories for more than a fortnight, and what did they do? Wriggle and fidget and say, "Why don't we *play* something?" Then they kept using those funny naughty street words, and Nurse would look up from her tatting and have to scold them. Melinda held her breath every time Nurse did this, because she was so afraid Mamma would hear about it and not let Melinda see Debby, Dave, and Danny any more.

It was not until Mr. Johnson had told Mamma what he

did that she had permitted Melinda to begin the readings in Mr. John's shop. Mr. Johnson had said, "It is a benevolent scheme of Newbery's, Madam, to let your little maid instill a love of books in those street waifs. Miss can take no harm and may do much good."

Melinda shook her head. Perhaps Mr. John was right, and there *was* still something wrong with his books. Debby, Dave, and Danny *didn't* like them; that was certain. Why, she wasn't at all sure that they would even turn up today for a reading. Oh, dear! If only she could think up some way to help Mr. John make books that the Monks couldn't help liking! If only she could!

"Did I just now hear a sigh? And from my very best customer?"

Melinda spun round. Mr. John stood there.

"Good morning," she said. "A very nice day. I am waiting for Debby and Dave and Danny."

"The question is, though, will they come?" The smile had gone from Mr. John's face now. "I fear they are much more interested in the pennies they earn with their muffins than in learning about any fairy gold in books."

"I fear so, too, Mr. John." Melinda spoke sadly.

"And the way Goldsmith and Griffith Jones and I labored over those books!" He was beating one fist against the other.

"Well, Johnson was right in trying to dissuade me. My books are still too dreary, too full of preachments."

"But, Mr. John, think of all the boys and girls who come here, clamoring for them!" She must try to cheer him.

"No, my dear, it is their parents who clamor for them, not the children. Even if half the nurseries in London own the books, they have still failed."

"It seems as if it would take a fairy to write any book that Debby and Dave and Danny would want to read."

Mr. John smiled. "I do not think the little Monks could tell a fairy if they saw one. They are businessmen."

"Oh, but they could. They pretend they meet ogres and princesses and fight battles whilst they sell their muffins, and—"

Melinda broke off. A fierce voice was coming from the doorway. It said, "Catsmeat Nan had best mend her ways this very day, or she'll be monstrous sorry. Selling her old scraps right afront o' the shop."

"Bless me! Debby and her brothers, and all in a flurry! I vow I thought a storm had blown in the door."

"Gave her a piece of my mind, I did."

"I'd like to box her ears."

"Come, children, calm down. Sit here on the bench and catch your breath before Melinda takes you into the back room and reads to you."

"We just came for the mugs of milk, Master Newbery,"
Debby said. "We'd as lief take poison as listen to more book
reading."

Danny nodded his head violently. "I'd lay a pound to a
penny Catsmeat Nan never stuck her nose inside a book, and
she able to bamboozle pennies out of half London."

"A muffiner dursn't waste time reading." It was Dave's turn now. "Misses trade if he does."

"Melinda, do you hear that?" Mr. Newbery was sighing to himself.

"They are naughty and—and ungrateful." Suddenly Melinda's eyes were shooting sparks, her foot was tapping the floor. "They don't know that you wrote some of those books, Mr. John."

"Master Newbery did!" Debby was staring at him, mouth open. "Be you a real author, sir?"

Dave marched resolutely to the bookcase and said, "Tell us which books you writ, and we'll listen to every one of them, sir. We know who got us these fine new clothes."

"Mother was fit to dance with joy when we moved into our grand new lodgings with the window tax all paid and plenty of sea-coal to burn," said Danny. "Bring on your books!"

John didn't know whether to be pleased or sorry. "Dear me," he said. "Dear me, I don't know what to say. I am very much touched by your gratitude, but I would wish you to read for the love of books, not for the love of me. Is there no kind of story you delight in?"

"Oh, stories," said Debby. "That's not like books. Stories are fun."

" 'Tis tales that fair curdle a body's blood that I like," Dave said. He smacked his lips. "Shipwrecks and smugglers and folks shouting their heads off, and Robin Hood a-coming to the rescue and pirates and highwaymen and dragons to kill and—" But then Dave had to stop to catch his breath.

"You give *me* lords and ladies and gold coaches fair bursting with jewels and velvet cushions. There'd be a book would make a body want to learn her A.B.C.'s." Debby and the feather were both bouncing up and down. "An honest-to-goodness princess, too, one who had a honeybird that sat on her shoulder and took nips at her lips, and the princess always wearing the beautifulest shoes."

"Princess, pah!" said Danny scornfully. "*I* like folks that do something, poor folk that make their way in the world and become rich and great and ride in coaches. You'd ought to write a book about a poor orphan boy—"

"A girl, a girl," cried Debby. "A girl that makes her own living in the world all by herself and—"

"Not a girl, a boy that goes off to sea and fights lots of battles and comes home a captain with a sword by his side," said Dave. "That's what *I'd* like."

"Perhaps you or Mr. Goldsmith *could* write a book like that." Melinda was looking beggingly at Mr. John. "Do please try."

THE dress was made of pink India muslin, and there were tiny loops of forget-me-nots and ribbons sprinkled over the skirt. Melinda stood there staring at it in a long wall mirror.

Goodness! She looked almost grown-up. Well, of course

CHAPTER *Thirteen*

she just had to look different when she was nine years old. Yesterday, when she was only eight, she was a little girl; she played with dolls and worked on her sampler. But now! Melinda's skirt came down to her shoe tops, and Mamma had put dabs of musk behind her ears. She was going to be allowed to stay up for the dinner party!

It would probably be the most wonderful party in all London; weren't Mr. and Mrs. Newbery, *Doctor* Johnson— Papa said Trinity College in Dublin had given him a degree— and Joshua Reynolds and Mr. Goldsmith all going to be there? It made Melinda quite proud to think that she had known Mr. Goldsmith before he was at all famous. He was such a funny, nice man.

Melinda whirled around to make her skirt fly out and almost danced into Mamma's dressing room. Mamma was putting a patch on her cheek. She turned to Melinda with an anxious frown. "Has the curl at the back of my left ear come loose, child? Look and see."

"No, ma'am, you look beautiful."

And Mamma did. How Melinda wished that Debby could have seen her! She had taken Melinda to the hairdresser's, and Melinda had watched, breathless, as he powdered and pomaded Mamma's hair, built it higher and higher with rolls and cushions, then pinned on puffs and curls, and, lastly, decorated it with a tiny model of a ship. Gracious! That headdress must be a whole yard high. When they had driven home, Mamma had had to sit on the floor of the coach so that her hair wouldn't hit the roof, and last night she had gone to bed with her head in a *basket*.

Oh, but the gown Mamma was wearing this evening! It was made of quilted brocade, the color of apple blossoms, and trimmed with Flemish lace. There were tiny black patches on her face, and she had a new fan of chicken skin. She rustled as she walked out of the room.

Papa was waiting for them at the foot of the stairs. "Gad, my pet, you are the very tulip of fashion," he said. "And here is another." He bowed very low to Melinda, and Melinda made her very best curtsy. Then the doorbell rang, and she ran upstairs as the first guests were announced, for she was not to come down until just before dinner.

Melinda sat down very carefully and puffed out her blue sash again. If Debby were here, *she* would be wearing a red dress, one with tassels, and of course her feather. Debby liked bright colors so much, and she had said she was going to dye her feather orange. What fun it must be to own a feather like that! How Melinda wished she could invite the Monks to her own house! Of course the boys would have giggled when they saw the ship on Mamma's hair. But she liked to hear them laugh and say funny things right out loud. They made her feel so gay and—and dancy inside. Mr. John was right: she was just a sobersides, and when she grew up and went to balls, not a single gentleman would ask her to dance.

There was pretty tinkling music coming from the drawing room. Mamma must be playing the spinet for the guests. Perhaps she, Melinda, could just slip inside without being noticed and find a seat next to Mr. John. No, of course she couldn't; she would have to curtsy first to everyone. Oh, why was she so shy? Debby never was.

Melinda opened the door. She stood there blushing, holding out her wide skirts, and curtsying. And she hadn't just slipped inside, because the gentlemen *were* all looking at her. They were standing up and bowing, with their hands on their hearts. Oh, *dear!*

"Why, Newbery, you never told me that your little book-worm was a beauty," said a deep voice.

That must be Dr. Johnson, and he was coming over to her. What a queer-looking man he was! He was very big, his face was covered with little pockmarks, his lips were thick, his clothes untidy, and he walked in a rolling sort of way. Papa said he sometimes went for a walk at four o'clock and didn't come home until two in the morning. He was thinking what to write in his books, she supposed.

"Sir, I think you must be Dr. Johnson," she said, her cheeks growing rosier and rosier, what with everyone looking. "Mr. Goldsmith has told me all about your cat, Hodge." Why, his gray wig was scorched in places. Did he bend too close to the candle when he was writing?

"Hodge would purr with pride if he could hear you. It gives me pleasure to meet so sweet a little maid." He had taken both her hands in his and smiled at her. His smile gave you a nice surprised feeling.

Now Mr. Goldsmith hurried over. He was dressed in a magnificent cherry-colored coat, and he bowed very low. "May I claim the privilege of old acquaintance, Mistress Melinda? You are so fine I hardly know you, but I am sure you will not let Johnson's gallantries win you away from old friends. Mistress Pratt, pray indulge us with a minuet on the spinet. I would beg the favor of a dance with your little maid."

"La, Mr. Goldsmith," Mamma said. "You are cosseting the child. But I am at your command, though you must remember that dinner will be served in a little time."

"We must not make dinner wait when John Newbery is here," said Dr. Johnson with great gravity. "Did I ever tell you, Goldy, that my Idler paper on Jack Whirler was founded on the character of our friend John Newbery? He sits down and fills his plate, but before the first morsel is in his mouth, hears the clock strike and rises; then goes to another house, sits down again, recollects another engagement, has only time to taste the soup, makes a short excuse to the company, and continues through another street his desultory dinner. Mistress Pratt, you may consider yourself fortunate tonight if he remains long enough to finish the soup."

"I fear you are right." Mr. John was blushing very red and twiddling with a coat button. "The one great trouble with life, I find, is that there is never time enough to do everything one wants to."

"But time for one dance with Mistress Melinda you must allow me, Madam," said Mr. Goldsmith, and Mamma started to play at once. Melinda and Mr. Goldsmith bowed, they walked and crossed over, and, oh, it was such great fun! Mr. Goldsmith seemed to like it, and he would pretend he was her partner and then that he was dancing with someone else on the other side. Then the music stopped, though, and suddenly Melinda felt dreadfully shy, because everybody was clapping. She slipped over to the blue satin couch where Mr. John sat.

"I am proud of you, Melinda," he said. "Was it fun pretending you were a grown-up lady?"

"Yes, but now I would wish to be a little girl and talk to you, Mr. John."

They didn't say anything else for a while then. Mr. John

seemed to be looking around at his friends as if he couldn't believe his eyes. Was he remembering about once being a little
boy and living in the country and wishing he could know some

real authors? Now he must know almost every author in London, and many other famous people, too. The nice-looking man who was talking to Mrs. Newbery was the fashionable portrait-painter, Joshua Reynolds.

But now Dr. Johnson's booming voice had caught Mr. John's attention, and Melinda listened, too. "There is now less flogging in our great schools than formerly, but then less is learned there; so that what the boys get at one end they lose at the other." Melinda shuddered. She did not hear what the gentlemen on the other side said next, but something about encouraging improving reading, for Dr. Johnson said, "I am always for getting a boy forward in his learning, for that is a sure good. I would let him at first read *any* English book which happens to engage his attention; because you have done a great deal when you have brought him to have entertainment from a book. He'll get better books afterwards."

"Mr. Newbery and Mr. Goldsmith have been active in the production of little books to catch a child's fancy," said Papa, with a bow towards Mr. John. "One is inscribed as 'To all young gentlemen and ladies who are good or intend to be good' by 'their old friend in St. Paul's Churchyard.' What is that rhyme on the title page of your little history of Mistress Margery Two Shoes, Melinda? I remember picking up that little book the other day and thinking it very amusing."

Melinda clasped her hands in her lap and took a deep breath. "It says the story is for those

'Who from a state of Rags and Care
And having Shoes but half a pair;
Their fortune and their Fame would fix,
And gallop in a Coach and Six.' "

There, that was over! But Dr. Johnson was making a rumbling sound. "Babies do not want to be told about other babies; they like to be told of giants and castles, and of somewhat which can stretch their little minds."

Mrs. Newbery tossed her head. "*The Circle of the Sciences* is in its tenth edition, and *Goody Two Shoes* is having a great sale."

"Remember always that the parents buy the books and the children never read them."

"*I* read them," said Melinda. She blushed and looked down. How often she had been told that children should not speak until they are spoken to! "I liked *Goody Two Shoes*," she said timidly.

Mr. John looked sad. Was he thinking of Debby and Dave and Danny, who had not liked the book even though it was about an orphan girl who made her own living in the world? They had been thoroughly disgusted that Goody Two Shoes made her fortune by teaching babies their letters.

"I am unsatisfied still." Mr. John was sighing. "I am un-satisfied with all my children's books."

"Sir, you have pleased Mistress Melinda, and I own my-self mistaken. No doubt you will soon hit upon other fancies that will please other little misses." Dr. Johnson rolled him-self in his chair complacently. "I have sometimes thought of trying my hand at this species of little fable myself."

Oliver Goldsmith gave him a comical look. "If you were to write a fable about the little fishes, you would make them talk like *great whales!* But John Newbery knows his own business better than any man in London, and his prosperity has been very generously shared. Where would you and I be, and many another poor author, if it were not for Newbery? He calls himself the friend of children, but he is the friend of all mankind."

"Nay, sir, that is not to the purpose of our argument: that will as much prove that he can play upon the fiddle as well as Giardini as that he can catch the imagination of children. But you deserve Goldy's praise, sir." He suddenly heaved himself around in his chair to face Mr. John. Gracious! Mamma looked as if she feared for the chair. "You have in-deed been a patron of distressed authors."

Mr. John was quite red with pleasure, but poor Mr. Gold-smith looked rather dashed. Melinda put out her hand to him, and he moved his chair beside her. "I *wish* he would not call me Goldy," he said pettishly.

If only she could think of something nice to say to make him feel better. Papa thought his long poem, *The Traveller*, was as good as Johnson's *London* or *The Vanity of Human Wishes*, or even better. Should she say so?

But Mr. Goldsmith was already looking cheerful again. He was tearing the corners off a piece of paper—it looked like a bill—and turning toward her quite eagerly. "I remember your fondness for games, my dear. Well, just cast an eye on this one!"

He put a little paper cap on each of his forefingers and bobbed them behind the arm of the couch. Then he began to recite a rhyme:

> "There were two Blackbirds
>   Sat upon a Hill,
> The one was named Jack,
>   The other named Gill.
> Fly away, Jack,
>   Fly away, Gill,
> Come again, Jack,
>   Come again, Gill."

Melinda giggled. The little paper birds looked so comical fluttering on top of their fingers, and Mr. Goldsmith had such a funny face as he made them do it! She looked around to see

if anyone else was noticing, but they weren't.   They were all
staring at Mr. John, who had suddenly sprung out of his seat.
He seized Mr. Goldsmith's arm and shook it.

"Noll," he cried, *"what is that rhyme?"*

"Mind what you're doing, man.   Have a care for my fine
new coat that isn't even paid for yet!"   Mr. Oliver was looking
at Mr. John as if he thought he had lost his senses.

Mr. John let go, but he still looked excited.   "Where did
you get that rhyme?"

"My old nurse taught it me."

"Those old nurses know a deal more about what children like than all the horrid example books put together!
Rhymed lines, and things happening in them every blessed
second!"   Mr. John's face was beaming.   "Oliver," he said,
"I am going to publish those old songs!"

JOHN Newbery was trudging along the Mall,
the walk by St. James's Park. The paths had been freshly
strewn with sea shells, and then crushed by the roller. It was
a fine sunny day in late April. You could smell the lilacs and
new leaves. Fine ladies in silks and satins were taking the air

119

CHAPTER *Fourteen*

in their carriages. Children trundled hoops and played with their dogs, while nurses kept a watchful eye on matters. People were staring at a penny puppet show. A peddler called, "Hot cross buns, hot cross buns. One a penny, two a penny, hot cross buns."

A merry scene, but John saw nothing of it. Hands clasped behind his back, wig crooked, he strode along, deep in worried thought. It had been so easy at first to find children's rhymes; he had remembered some himself, and all his friends knew a few, though they were often the same ones. But now he was at his wit's end to know which way to turn. He knew there must be hundreds of old nursery songs, and he could not find fifty!

John ran his fingers through his wig and frowned. "If I didn't tell Granny once that her verses ought to be collected, because folks' memories could get holes in them at times, and the old songs be forgot! Of course she only sniffed at the idea of wasting time over cradle songs. She was wrong, though; I feel sure she was. And I was a simpleton not to have learned more of her old rhymes."

A ragged urchin held out a tin cup, and John stopped to find a penny. The boy snatched the coin, and as he scuttled away, John heard him say over his shoulder, "Now I can buy my mother suthin' to eat. God bless you, sir."

The beggar made John think of the three Monks. If those rhymes but served to make *them* want to learn to read, they would be worth his search. He loved the little imps. All they lived to do was to sell their muffins and play pranks on the other ragamuffins, but how merry and fearless they were! Just to hear them laugh—Melinda couldn't—was enough to make a man forget all his troubles. They knew nothing, though; not even their A.B.C.'s.

John sighed. Was it he or Melinda who had been the more disappointed when Debby, Dave, and Danny had refused even to look at Melinda's cardboard battledore, with the alphabet and all the old hornbook lessons? Nowadays the battledore was covered with gilt embossed Dutch paper, not at all like the dull wood and horn he and Henry Monk had studied from—and Queen Elizabeth before them, most like. The new battledores were being shipped in great quantities to the American Colonies. Well, he hoped the small boys and girls there were taking to them better than the Monks were. Alas for Henry's children; they didn't give a straw for *any* book. If they laid hands on a penny, they spent it on tarts or sugarplums.

Wouldn't the little Monks be surprised to find one of their own absurd rhymes in his book! Debby had come into the shop one day all full of something and offered to tell him a story. He had known it was a joke from the way the boys were grinning, but how very gravely Debby had begun her tale!

> "There was an old Man
> And he had a Calf,
> And that's Half;
> He took him out of the Stall
> And put him on the Wall . . .
> And that's all!"

John had not found this *quite* as funny as the three little Monks seemed to, but it deserved a place in his book for all that.

Trudging along now, John could not forget his pet scheme. The street was thick with peddlers, calling their wares, but he turned a deaf ear to them. "Brooms," they said, "pots, baskets, cold Molly puffs.". . . "Pretty maids, pretty pins.". . . "A bed mat or a door mat; lily white vinegar threepence a quart; twelve pennies a peck for oysters.". . . "Buy a white line, a jack line, a clothes line." "Ballads, news sheets, and chapbooks, good ladies, good sirs."

None of those were real rhymes. He had got a good one from the pig pie man, though:

> "A long tailed Pig, or a short tailed Pig,
>   Or a Pig without any Tail;
> A Sow Pig, or a Boar Pig,
>   Or a Pig with a curling Tail.
> Take hold of the Tail and eat off his Head;
> And then you'll be sure Pig hog is dead."

Noll Goldsmith had called his attention to that one. Whatever would I have done if it weren't for Goldsmith? John thought. Noll has not only written many of the best of my children's books but has managed to scrabble around in his memory and recall a good store of nursery rhymes—*Jack and Gill*, and the one that he liked so well:

> "Little Tom Tucker
> Sings for his Supper;
> What shall he eat?
> White Bread and Butter:
> How will he cut it,
> Without e'er a Knife?
> How will he be married,
> Without e'er a Wife?"

Noll was going to write a comical preface, using his favorite song of the old woman tossed in a blanket; and what fun it had been to choose maxims and notes to go with the verses! After "The little Dog laughed to see such Craft, And the Dish ran away with the Spoon," Oliver had put, "It must be a little Dog that laughed, for a great Dog would be ashamed to laugh at such Nonsense!"

John's rapid steps had slowed down by now. He studied a scrap of paper, then peered carefully around. This must be the street he was looking for; it seemed little more than a wide alley, though. It was so narrow that the shops and houses, with their overhanging roofs, were nodding across to one another, saying, "Mind if I stick my nose in?"

Here it was: Number 30. It *was* a convenience now the houses were numbered. Number 30 was a tiny bookshop with a dormer window. Good gracious! It was the size of a dog kennel. He went down two rickety steps and opened the door. He thought he must be standing in a cave. The only light came from an iron lantern hanging from the ceiling. He could just make out the piles of books that lay on counter, chairs, and shelves. John blinked; Melinda would certainly find her book-worms here. Mice, too, from the smell.

And then someone spoke to him in a small, squeaky voice: "May I be of assistance, sir?"

The speaker seemed to be scuttling out of some dark, mysterious hole. He was a tiny man, and he looked like a rabbit. His nose twitched as he spoke.

"I am searching for old rhymes and songs for children," John explained. "The kind that nurses have been amusing their charges with down the years."

"Ah!" said the little man. "Ah! A queer quest, sir, but I do not doubt you have a good reason for pursuing it." He rubbed his nose thoughtfully. "Some of them have been printed in old books of songs and catches— Wait!" He spun round and pulled a great dusty sheaf of old broadside ballads off a spike on the wall. "I remember how surprised I was to find *Three Children Sliding on the Ice* in the middle of a long lamentation about a bad winter back nearly a hundred years ago. Think of that!"

"I have that one," said John. Why, he had used the rhyme in *Tommy Trip* and never known it had been printed before! He put the untidy bundle down under the lantern and began leafing through it. He found one that began with a verse about a pudding pie woman that he'd heard said to children, but most of the broadsides seemed to be dying words and last confessions of famous highwaymen hanged at Tyburn and bad verses about news of the day. Here was one that sounded more like a song— "There was a little man who wooed a little maid." He put that aside with the pudding pie woman.

"This came out only a year or two ago, didn't it?" he said. "I seem to remember the broadside hawker singing it."

"Yes, in 1764," said the little man. "I take it you are looking for verses such as *Margery Daw?*"

"Margery Daw?" John had begun to beam. "Oliver Goldsmith sent me to you on the chance you might know some. Be kind enough to say the whole verse."

"That I will, that I will." He cleared his thin throat.

> "Se saw, Margery Daw,
>   Jacky shall have a new Master;
>   Jacky must have but a Penny a Day,
>   Because he can work no faster."

"Ah, thank you, sir, thank you." John drew a deep breath. "Could you recall any others?"

The little man was bouncing up and down on his heels. His lips nibbled for a second on some thought, and he said:

" 'Pears to me that my mother, God rest her soul, had one she said when I was scarce out of my cradle. Let me see! Let me see! Ah, yes! It ran:

> "One, two, three,
>   Four and Five,
> I caught a Hare alive;
> Six, seven, eight,
>   Nine and ten,
> I let him go again."

" 'Tis the kind I want," John told the little man. "Just the kind I want. Go on, I beg you."

"I do recall, sir,"—now the man was blushing—"that there was a verse my mother would repeat to my sister Hannah. You see, Hannah had a bit of a quick temper, and perhaps you know what rascals boys can be? I liked nothing better than to hear her get her comeuppance when—"

"Tell me the rhyme, sir," John broke in eagerly. "Tell me the rhyme."

"Ah, yes, the rhyme!

> "Cross Patch, draw the Latch,
> Set by the Fire and spin;
> Take a cup and drink it up,
> Then call your Neighbors in."

"Any more?" John was busily scribbling down the words, sighing happily. "Do you know any more?"

"Not at the moment, sir, not *precisely* at the moment." The little man whisked across to a bookshelf. "But there might be something in the chapbook, *Tom Hickathrift*." He was running his hand along the shelf. "Now, where in tunket did I put it? Tom Hickathrift, you may recall, was six feet tall and three feet wide at the age of ten, and he owned a hand like a shoulder of mutton—"

"No, the book is in prose, not verse." Again John interrupted. "Besides, I have already read it." Suddenly he felt like confiding in the little bookseller. He told about grave little Melinda, who needed to laugh; about the little Monks, who saw no pleasure in books; about his search for rhymes, his plans for the book. He was not the first to publish children's rhymes—there had been one or two little books of them published not too many years since, and he had even heard of one that came out twenty years ago, though he had not been able to get hold of it—but with Goldsmith's help, his book was to be something special, and he had great hopes for it.

The little man, chin in his hand, listened intently. His nose twitched now and then, his fingers pulled at the sides of his lips, just as if he were stroking rabbit whiskers, but he did not once speak until John had finished.

128

"The hodgepodge of things that stick in a man's memory," he said then. "It seems as if I mind my mother once saying that most of those rhymes came from the country. I wonder whether you—"

"The country!" John's face lighted up. "*I* wonder whether I have lost what senses I ever had. Why, sir, I happen to know the most wonderful country woman in all of England, or at least I once did, more's the shame! Dame Dorcas is her name, and she it was who taught me not only the love of reading, but every hope and dream I ever had. She taught school, and—"

"You have the notion, then, that she might help you—"

"I *know* that she can help me. There is naught she does not know when it comes to children. Sir, I have no words to thank you for reminding me of her. I shall go to see her in Berkshire straight off."

THE three horses galloped along the highway.
The new Flying Coach, called the Comet, rattled and jolted and
groaned. The black leather seats, with their broad-headed nails,
sloped towards the back of the coach, and the passengers sloped
with them.

CHAPTER *Fifteen*

Up on the roof perched the driver, cracking his whip and humming a tune. He never touched the horses with the whip, but now and then his lips made a sound that was like a stick struck against a wheel spoke. The horses knew what it meant, though: "Hurry up! Hurry up!" The guard beside the driver held his blunderbuss cocked, ready, in case some masked highwayman should gallop out from a side road. The young postilion rode the lead horse, and he too kept a sharp lookout for robbers.

Now they had left Maidenhead far behind and were coming close to Waltham St. Lawrence. Blooming hedges were beginning to flash past, fields gay with buttercups. Face pressed against the window, happy as a sandboy, John Newbery was recognizing one familiar sight after another. Forgotten were the dark and treacherous roads, the stones and ruts, mud and quagmires, the turnpikes with their pesky tolls, and his weary body.

There's the great house, he was saying to himself. Place where I used to carry wild strawberries for Squire, and not changed a whit. . . . The old parsonage where father and the other farmers came to pay their tithes, and then to fair stuff themselves with Parson's roast beef and apple dumplings. . . . I declare! The brook! Henry and I searched for watercress and tadpoles there and looked for wild fowls' eggs among the reeds. . . . That road yonder! We trod it that day we went to the fair. How old were we? Eleven years?

His eyes were shining, his fingers twitched. When he came back to Waltham St. Lawrence, he felt as if he had slipped back into his childhood; his grown-up years had folded up, had disappeared. His brother Robert's grown-up children never failed to surprise him—except for Francis, of course, who worked with him in London.

The stagecoach slowed. "S-o-o h-o-o!" the driver called to the horses. They drew up before the White Horse Inn in a gallant cloud of dust, and the young postilion leaped lightly to the ground. His trumpet blew a lively air. John popped out of the coach almost before the guard laid down his blunderbuss. The same old White Horse Inn where he used to borrow books from Henry's uncle! But of course it was a new innkeeper that came bustling forward to greet him now.

"Welcome, sir, welcome! Why, 'tis Mr. Newbery from London! 'Tis many a long day since we've seen you here, sir. I do trust you are not too weary? That you made the journey in fair comfort and no highwayman gave you concern?"

"Not a sign of the scoundrels, landlord," John said.

"Heaven be thanked for that! The tales the drivers tell fair chill your blood. You'll take a bite here before going up to the farm?"

"My thanks, but first I must make inquiry for the friend I am here to see," John said, and suddenly his voice was unsteady. What if— No, he wouldn't even think it. If she were dead, his quest would be in vain. And Waltham St. Lawrence without Dame Dorcas! The very notion made a blackness in his mind.

"And who might that be, sir?" said the innkeeper curiously. Squire himself, mayhap, he thought. They do say this Mr. Newbery be a rich man.

"Dame—Dame Dorcas. Once she taught school. Is she —is she—"

"Dame Dorcas, be it? Nigh on ninety, they say, but still spry and hale."

John let out a slow breath. Dame Dorcas was living! To think that he'd soon be talking to her again! . . . "Lad, read every single book you can lay hands on." He was whispering the words to himself and smiling. "We were having red currant jam and crumpets in her parlor."

The innkeeper was looking at him in wonder, mouth agape. "And how are my nephews and nieces?" John asked hastily.

"All well here, sir, and how be young Francis?"

"Both well," said John absently. "I mean both Francises —my brother's son and my own Frank." He was gazing eagerly around the little village green, his face glowing. There was the blacksmith's forge! You could hear the anvil ringing, and if there wasn't the same old rusty horseshoe hung over the door! Did he still forge plowshares as well as shoe horses? . . . That goose girl leading her geese to market. Like as not their feet were rubbed with tar, to harden them for the long walk. Molly Monk always said she was going to be a goose girl. Had her wish come true? . . . And Mistress Perkins's confection shop. Was it still selling those tarts and comfits, the twisted barley sticks that once made Henry Monk's mouth water so?

John turned to the innkeeper. "If it will not put you out, I think I'll not have dinner now. There is an important matter I must attend to." And he was off, hurrying down the street, looking eagerly right and left.

There is the old pound for stray animals, the same old ivy-covered oaks, and the old mill wheel turning merrily. What has happened to me? I feel just as if I were a boy going to a fair!

He had passed through the old gateway now and come to the highway. The same trees, the same benches set here and there for weary travelers. It is spring now, and the day that Henry and I came to the fair was September. . . . Would you look at that stretch of buttercups!

134

I told Henry, that September day, that I was going to London and get to know the famous writers. And Henry pushed out his lips and said, "Your wits are wandering. What you're going to do is stay here, same as me, and hoe and harrow and feed the pigs."

John gave a soft sigh. Suppose Henry had been right? Suppose he, John, *had* stayed here and been a farmer? And of course he would have done that, if it hadn't been for Dame Dorcas. Suddenly he felt himself breaking into a half-run. He couldn't wait another minute to see her.

It was half an hour later when John caught sight of the straw-thatched cottage, but it seemed to him like years. It was frozen there, he thought. It was like a woodcut from one of his books; it never changed. The hawthorn tree in bloom, like some pink canopy, the old holly tree by the door.

CHAPTER *Sixteen*

John's heart hammered as he knocked on the door. There was a sound inside, and the door opened. A tiny figure stood there. She was dressed in gray linsey-woolsey, she had a white shawl about her shoulders and a snowy mobcap on her head.

"Dame! Dame *Dorcas!*" John cried.

"Bless me! 'Tis—'tis John Newbery." Her cracked voice stopped, as if she couldn't go on. Her face was working.

"Then you remember me!" Why, she seemed hardly changed at all! She leaned on a cane, and her face was as wrinkled as a walnut, but her cheeks were still rosy and her black eyes bright.

"Remember you! Think I could forget John Newbery? But come you in, lad. Come you in. 'Tis—'tis a sight for sore eyes, seeing you after all these years." She stopped; she was frowning. "Mercy me!" she said, after a moment. "Can't make out why there be tears in my eyes. Must be that smoke from the chimney. Hasn't been drawing too well."

They were in the little parlor now, and nothing had changed here. The same three-legged chairs, the stuffed owl that stared at you wherever you were, the dried leaves on the mantel shelf. And the books! That scent, it must be from the jar of pressed rose petals; he could smell the spices. Why —why, he could hear words! "What would you say, lad, if I gave you an introduction to William Carnan in Reading?

Might be he could teach you how to be a printer."

" 'Tis like coming home, Dame Dorcas," John said.

"Sit you down in that chair and tell me all about yourself. 'Tis but once in a blue moon that Waltham St. Lawrence can welcome a London publisher."

"If it had not been for you, I'd still be milking cows and feeding pigs." Now it was John's eyes that seemed to be having trouble with the smoke. He was blowing his nose very hard.

"Stuff and nonsense! Don't you be trying to butter me up, John." She was trying, John could tell, to sound stern and like a teacher. Only, she wasn't quite succeeding. She cleared her throat. "Hmph! I expect by now you are on friendly terms with many a writer in London Town. I should like well to hear about this Samuel Johnson. Is he all that he is painted in the way of book-learning?"

"More, Dame Dorcas, more. Besides that, he is my friend —so are Oliver Goldsmith, Joshua Reynolds, and the actor, David Garrick. But it is of you I would hear. Is all well with you?"

Dame Dorcas sniffed. She sniffed exactly the way she did when Molly Monk couldn't read the hornbook lesson or Henry had fallen asleep over his sums.

"And why should not things go well?" she asked. "Do I

not live in the finest county in England? What other town, pray, but Waltham St. Lawrence, owns a place like Castle Acres, where there was a Roman fort, or a manor house that can hold a candle to the squire's? Of course—" now she was looking down—"I am an old woman now, and there are times when my bones do ache with the rheumatics. 'Tis nothing, though. Farmer Skelton vows 'tis caused by nothing more than a small leak in the roof, where the rain gets in."

"A leak in the roof! Then you may forget that." John was speaking quickly and eagerly. "I shall see to it that you have a fine new roof you can be proud of."

"Tut, now! Just why should you be—"

"Dame Dorcas, listen to me." John was leaning towards her, his hands clasping and unclasping. "That day I started off for Reading, I made a vow. It was one day to buy you the very finest silken gown in all Berkshire. I—I never did buy it, though. I'm ashamed to say it, too. Why—why, everything I've ever done is due to you."

"Buttering me up again." Dame Dorcas's fingers were twisting. "I did naught but teach you how to read and cast up sums, with a smidgeon of history thrown in for good measure. The will to succeed was in you, lad. Why, I knew even then that one day you would make a name for yourself. I am proud of you, John Newbery. I—I'll go farther. I'll tell you that you always were to me the dearest of all my pupils."

John couldn't speak. His lips were trembling. Her words had made him feel even prouder than he had when he opened his shop at the Bible and Sun.

"It seems to me that I remember everything you did or said." Dame Dorcas was going on. "Like the time you proposed to make me a pair of spectacles with one rim flavored with peppermint and the other with licorice. I like to have burst my sides laughing at the thought of it."

And suddenly Dame Dorcas was laughing now, and John was laughing, too. And then he had begun to tell her all about his search for the nursery rhymes and what the little bookseller had advised him to do. Dame Dorcas sat there listening, hardly saying a word. Her thin hands lay clasped in her lap; her tiny feet in their felt slippers were set close together; her bright eyes were fixed on his face. Even when he had finished, Dame Dorcas did not speak for a long minute. She had always been a listening person. Then she said slowly:

"Parson is forever telling us that confession is good for the soul. Be that as it may, I am about to confess something to you, John. There have been times of late—it may be age has softened me—when I have thought I may once have been too ready with the birch. When Molly Monk's youngest drops in to see me, with a nosegay of buttercups clutched in her hand—

know what it will be made up of, Dame Dorcas? Those of—
of 'that Nurse of Art and Humours, Master William Shake-
speare!' "

Dame Dorcas nodded approvingly.

"And now all that I need is your help." John went on.
"Tell me, *can* you recall any of the rhymes?"

"There—there is naught I'd like so well as to help set
words in a book." Dame Dorcas's cheeks had grown rosier
than ever. " 'Twould be like a dream beyond my fondest
hopes, John. There's one trouble, though. My memory at
times is fitful-like. I tell you what I shall do. I always remember best when I am supping a dish of tea—Squire is kind enough
to keep me supplied with the leaves—and I do have a loaf of
spiced gingerbread and a jar of red currant jam in the cool
room, all sealed down, too, with a bit of pig's bladder, to keep
it sweet— Now, where am I?—Oh, yes, I know what I wanted
to say. Suppose I go set the kettle on the hook, and we have
tea? Then I'll don my thinking cap and see how many rhymes
I can call to mind."

Dame Dorcas put on her thinking cap to good purpose.
She remembered seven rhymes: *Bah, Bah, Black Sheep; Ride a
Cock Horse to Banbury Cross; This Pig Went to Market, That
Pig Stayed at Home; Cock a Doodle Doo, My Dame Has Lost
Her Shoe; Shoe the Colt, Shoe the Colt; There Was an Old*

Woman Lived Under a Hill (not the one he already had, but a different one); and *Ding Dong Bell, The Cat Is in the Well.*

When, an hour later, John stood up to go, he felt content. Now he would have forty-seven rhymes for his book. There were a few pages left, but surely—surely—he would somewhere find another three or four rhymes!

He wanted to thank Dame Dorcas, but he didn't know how to do it. To thank her not only for the rhymes, but just for being still herself. Because it was to her that he—and how many other boys and girls?—owed what they were today. She had pluck and patience and strength of purpose, and she had given them to him as simply, as without any thanks asked, as she had those crumpets spread with jam, that day so long ago.

I have been ungrateful, I have forgot her, John said to himself, but I shall make it up to her now. I'll have that roof repaired in short order, and she shall have the best new dress my wife can find in London Town. John smiled. I think I know, though, what she would treasure more, and she shall have it. The first *Mother Goose's Melody* that comes from my presses is going to be hers. I'll write my love and respect for her on the flyleaf, and when I present the book, my wife and the three little Monks will be with me.

*J*OHN put down the old copy of *Pilgrim's Progress* that Samuel Johnson had ordered, and lit his pipe. There was so thick a fog outside that wisps of it had even crept into the shop. From far away came the beat of drums, guiding boats to shore.

CHAPTER *Seventeen*

Candles were lit in the room, a fire crackled briskly on the wide hearth, the rows of books gleamed invitingly, and John should have felt very cozy and secure. He didn't, though.

Here it was months since he had returned from Waltham St. Lawrence, and so far he had not found any more rhymes. He was at heart a country boy, and he felt shy asking strangers a favor. Sometimes, walking in Hyde Park, he had heard nurses singing songs to children, and he had wanted to ask them what they were singing, but it seemed as if something always held him back.

Dame Dorcas had told him to have patience. Noll Goldsmith had reminded him that Rome was not built in a day. Then why not admit it? Whenever he set out to do anything, he was fair eaten with impatience until he had done it. Johnson had been right when he named him "Jack Whirler."

But this time he had been patient; he had put the book aside, hoping for more nursery rhymes, until it was almost too late to hurry it through before Christmas. No doubt Goldsmith could find or write very good rhymes for those empty pages, but John had set his heart on having this book just as he had imagined it.

John was banging the pages of *Pilgrim's Progress* together, not seeing the little cloud of dust that came whirling out. Hadn't he, all ready and waiting, the woodcuts for the verses he did have? Hadn't he decided on the size, and the color of the cover? Whenever he went into the printing shop, it seemed as if the presses growled at him, "Give us that book, John. Give us that book."

He was so lost in thought that when a voice said "Good morning," he looked up with a start.

Melinda stood there. He had not even heard the bell tinkle when she came in.

"Appearances are a bit against its being a good morning, Melinda," he said, "what with that pesky fog and all. Only, *you* look as if it pleased you. Your cheeks are as rosy as those flames, and your eyes are dancing."

"And I feel all rosy inside me, Mr. John." Melinda had pulled off her tippet and sat down by the fire. "You see, I have a present for you. A very nice present, too."

"Not a bookworm, wrapped in that mitten, I trust?" John's eyes had begun to twinkle. He had grown very fond of Melinda.

"Oh, no, much better than that." She looked as proud as a peacock. "You told me, Mr. John, that you still need rhymes for your book. Well, I have found you some. I have found four."

"Found *four!*" John stood there without moving, hearing his breath coming queerly. "Where? What are they?

147

Oh, Melinda, you don't know how I thank you!"

"They have a little story, sir, and may I tell it first?"

The little minx! She might have taken a lesson in acting from David Garrick, making that pause before she said something important. John bit his lip. Then he said, "Certainly, my dear. What is the story?"

"I knew that you couldn't find those rhymes anywhere, and I have worried very much. Nurse scolded me because I couldn't finish my supper, and Mamma made me take a dose of that horrid French cold tea. How dreadful it would be, I thought, if Debby and Dave and Danny never learned to read because they couldn't ever have a chance to see your book. I was anxious, too, about those little boys and girls away across the sea in the American Colonies. What with all those bears and wolves and wild Indians, it does seem as if we ought to do *something* to make them forget their troubles, and—"

"But the rhymes, Melinda, the *rhymes!*"

Melinda, though, was not to be hurried. She clasped her mittened hands in her lap and gave a sigh.

"You know, sir, that I am a very shy girl. Mamma says that I can't say 'Boo' to a goose. Whenever I try to speak to a stranger, it seems as if—it seems as if icy cold prickles run up and down my back—"

"I know, my dear, I know. I am the same way. It takes

the little Monks to be unafraid of anyone or anything."

"Yes, it does, Mr. John. But you see I was determined to find you some more rhymes. I feel that I am your partner in this book, and besides, I don't know what I'd ever have done if you hadn't introduced me to Debby and Dave and Danny. They're so exciting!"

"They are, aren't they? But go on."

"Yes, I will—I mean I am. It was just yesterday, and I had gone to see Christopher. He is the little brother of that cousin of mine who always gives herself a higher mark in school than I do. I told you about her once, you remember. Christopher doesn't know anything about marks, though. He is the cuddliest little boy; he just sits there smiling and smiling, and—"

"Melinda, what of the rhymes?" John could hardly sit still.

"Well, Christopher has a new nurse, Mr. John. She comes from the country, and she's rosy and smells of clover, and when I went into the nursery, I could hardly believe my ears. Do you know what she was doing?"

"*No!*"

"She was singing a rhyme as she rocked Christopher in her arms, and he was making purring sounds, and all of a sudden I didn't feel shy or afraid. Isn't that funny, Mr. John?"

"Very funny, Melinda."

"I just drew one long breath, and then I asked her to sing the song again very slowly, so that I could write it down. And she did, and I think you will see that it is one of the nicest rhymes you have ever—"

"Say it, child. *Say* it." John was groaning.

"Yes, sir. It goes:

> "Hush a by Baby
>   On the Tree Top,
> When the Wind blows
>   The Cradle will rock.
> When the Bough breaks
>   The Cradle will fall,
> Down tumbles Baby,
>   Cradle and all."

"There, Mr. John. Do you like it?"

"Hush a by Baby On the tree top! Yes, I do like it. I do." John let out a long breath; he was beaming. "And there are others?"

"Oh, yes, three, but the laughy verse is the one I like best. I know Debby and Dave and Danny will like *it*. It goes:

> "Dickery, Dickery Dock,
> The Mouse ran up the Clock;
> The Clock struck one,
> The Mouse ran down,
> Dickery, Dickery Dock.

150

"Then there's one about Jack Sprat, who could eat no fat
—Papa is just like that, and Mamma scolds him—and the last is
Bow, wow, wow, Whose Dog art thou? Little Tom Tinker's
Dog, Bow, wow, wow, and—and that's all, Mr. John."

"Melinda, Melinda, how can I ever thank you?" John
sprang up and flung his arms around her. "I have fifty-one
rhymes. I can finish my book!"

I T WAS snowing again. Again the streets
looked like a great bed spread with a white coverlet. In the
little room behind the bookshop, though, it might have been
summer, it looked so warm and gay. That, at least, was what
John Newbery thought as he opened the door and peered in.

152

CHAPTER *Eighteen*

The room seemed to be overflowing with children and laughter and voices and books. Melinda sat by the fire; she was reading aloud from a book, a small book covered with flowery paper. Flat on her back on the floor lay Debby, a book in *her* hand. Bouncing up and down on the groaning sofa was Dave, and he was waving aloft a small book. And Danny, standing on the top of a chair, apparently trying to reach the wall clock, was holding a book under his chin.

John waited before he went in. None of them had noticed him; they were far too busy to look around.

Melinda said, reading from her book:

> "Dickery, Dickery Dock,
>   The Mouse ran up the Clock—

"Have you run up it, Danny? You're the mouse."

"I be close to it," shouted Danny. "Keep on."

> "The Clock struck one—"

"Bong!" went Debby's spoon against the tin collection cup—

> "The Mouse ran down—"

Danny gave a wild spring up the wall. His fingers touched the clock; then he toppled. He was lying flat on the floor.

"Dickery, Dickery Dock," Dave called, and jounced twice on the sofa.

153

Laughter filled the little room. Danny and Dave and Debby were laughing so they could hardly speak, and so was Melinda Pratt!

"You're the very noisiest mouse *I* ever heard." Melinda was wiping her eyes. "What are those strings hanging from your mouth? Whiskers?"

"Like to have broke his crown, he was, when he hit the floor." Debby was rolling over and over, laughing.

"*I* thought he'd pulled down the clock a-top o' him, sure as eggs is eggs, I did," Dave screamed gleefully. "Didn't I come in good on 'Dickery, dickery dock?'"

"I know—I know! Let's do *High diddle, diddle*." Debby had jumped to her feet and was whirling around in circles. "I'll be the cow that jumped over the moon. You can be the moon, Danny, and—"

"Not I," shouted Danny. "I'm going to be the cow—"

"I have it." Melinda was dancing up and down in her excitement. "You can be the dish *and* the spoon, Danny. Dave will be the cat and play the fiddle, and Debby will jump over the footstool—the moon. I'll be the little dog that laughed, because I know just how a little dog would laugh, and—"

"And now *you* know how to laugh, too." John came into the room as he spoke. His eyes were shining.

And then they had pounced on him, all shouting together.

154

"Did you hear me being the mouse?" "Did you hear my *bong?*" "We've been playing all the best songs in Mother Goose." "Watch me, watch me! I'm going to be the cow jumping over the moon." They dragged John over to the sofa and piled on top of him.

"Help!" he said, throwing up his hands. "Help, Help!"

"We won't play, Mr. John; we'll show you something." Melinda was panting with excitement as she picked up a pair of John's spectacles from the table and stuck them on her nose. "Now, children"—she turned to the Monks, a fierce frown on her face—"you may all take your seats. The spelling lesson is about to begin. Debby, spell 'cat.' "

"C-a-t," Debby said promptly. "Pough! 'Tis easy."

"Very good. Danny, you spell 'cow.' "

"C-o—" Danny stopped and scratched his head; then he beamed triumphantly and shouted, "C-o-w. *I* don't have to wear that dunce's cap, do I, Teacher?"

Melinda shot a proud glance at John, and then she turned to Dave. "Now it is your turn. Spell 'mouse.' "

Dave wriggled in his chair and scowled. "It be'ent fair," he protested. "Danny only had 'cow.' "

Silently Melinda's lips spelt, "m-o-u—"

John's mouth twitched. Hadn't he once helped Molly Monk that way?

155

"M-o-u-s-e," Dave crowed. "'Tis easy as rolling off a log."

"Did you hear that, Mr. John? They can spell real words." Melinda's spectacles were hanging on the tip of her nose; she was beaming from ear to ear. "And do you know how they learnt?   From the alphabet song in *Mother Goose's Melody*, and from

> "Great A, little a,
>   Bouncing B;
> The Cat's in the Cupboard,
>   And she can't see!"

"Bless me!   Then pigs *can* fly!   Debby, Dave, and Danny are learning their letters at last!"   John was laughing, but there seemed to be a knot in his throat, and he had to swallow it.

"Easy as breathing."   Debby tossed her head briskly. "Melinda reads us a rhyme and we play it out, and then she helps us spell the words.   We can spell monstrous hard words now, and we'll soon be a-reading for ourselves."

"Wait till you can read *Mother Goose's Tales*," said Melinda eagerly.   "Blue Beard and The Sleeping Beauty and Puss in Boots and—"

"*Mother Goose's Melody* first, and a rare good book it is, too," said Dave.   He gave a shout and clapped Danny on the back.   "What'll Catsmeat Nan say when she *sees* us reading that book?"

"With our names writ in it, too," Danny said.

Once again John heard that sound he loved so much— Melinda's laugh.   She didn't say anything, though.   Now she

157

was looking at him. And it seemed at that moment something closer than words passed between them.

John felt his heart swell with pride. At last he had given children a gift worth having. Something inside him seemed to say, "Your melodies will never die, John Newbery, while there are children that can laugh, and nurses who sing."